The Food Safety Book

THE FOOD SAFETY BOOK

What You Don't Know Could Kill You

Joe Kivett and Dr. Mark Tamplin
with Dr. Gerald J. Kivett

CONSTANT ROSE PUBLISHING

Orlando

2016

© 2016 Kivett Productions, Inc.

The Food Safety Book
First Edition, Paperback – published 2016
Constant Rose Publishing
ISBN 978-0-9791741-0-0
Not for resale.

10 9 8 7 6 5 4 3 2 1

Book design, Clay Rivers

Dedicated to the thousands of people who strive to keep our food supply safe, and the medical community who helps us recover from foodborne illness.

An ounce of prevention is worth a pound of cure.

—BENJAMIN FRANKLIN

Contents

Acknowledgments

The authors would like to thank:

Dr. Gerald J. Kivett for
his valuable contributions to the foodborne illness section
of this book.

Special thanks to Cris Novoa
for the hundreds of hours of research
she put into this project.

We would also like to thank Angie Ritti, Melinda Wilson,
Priscilla Smith, and our friends and family who reviewed
the book and provided beneficial feedback.

Jo McAtee
for amazing proofing and editing contributions.

Our publisher, Clay Rivers,
the final piece of the puzzle,
who brought this book to life.

And finally,
Joe would like to thank his mom, Helen Kivett,
for being a great role model in the kitchen
and for always knowing.

Introduction

There are hundreds of websites, articles, books, and brochures that focus on food safety. Some have vast amounts of information, more than the average consumer needs or wants. Other sources are very specialized, with a great deal of information on a specific topic. We feel that *The Food Safety Book* offers consumers a simple, one-stop reference for basic issues regarding food safety.

The primary goal of this publication is to provide consumers with information that will help reduce their chances of falling victim to a foodborne illness (food poisoning). In addition, this guide will provide useful information about food storage and longevity that will save consumers valuable shopping dollars.

The Food Safety Book covers three key themes:

1 **Food Safety**: How to handle, thaw, cook, and store food in ways that reduce the likelihood of acquiring food-borne illness.
2 **Food Quality**: How to select, transport, and store food so that it remains fresh and tastes great.
3 **Food Longevity:** Easy-to-read charts that outline how long foods last in different environments (shelf, refrigerator, freezer).

Please keep in mind that the information contained in this publication should be used only as a guide. Most importantly, always use common sense before consuming food products—in other words, if you are not certain that your food is safe to eat, throw it away. **When in doubt, throw it out!** It's not worth taking a chance on consuming bad food that could cause foodborne illness and lead to serious illness or even death.

We hope that the information in *The Food Safety Book* will enable you, your family, and your friends to enjoy safe, fresh, and great-tasting food.

Please note, this book is based on information and regulations found in the United States. Some data may not apply to other countries.

Finally, we ask that you tell your friends about this book so they, too, can enjoy safe eating. Friends and family can order the book on our website at www.thefoodsafetybook.com.

Sincerely,
Joe Kivett
Dr. Mark Tamplin
Dr. Gerald J. Kivett

The Four Basic Concepts of Food Safety

Public health reports indicate that a high percentage of foodborne illness in the U.S. is caused by mistakes made in the home. Consumers can prevent foodborne illness by following these four basic concepts:

- **Separate**: Keep raw meat, poultry, seafood, and their juices away from ready-to-eat food. Most importantly, contain meat juices within their package.
- **Clean**: Keep anything that contacts food (hands, countertops, cutting boards, etc.) clean and sanitary by regularly washing hands and using clean and sanitized food utensils and hand towels.
- **Cook**: Cook all foods to the proper minimum internal cooking temperature.
- **Chill or Heat**: Never leave perishable foods in the Danger Zone (between 40°–140°F) for more than two hours. If there is any doubt about the safety of food, do **not** eat it. **When in doubt, throw it out!**

Reminders:

- Check storage directions on labels.
- Refrigerate or freeze perishables right away.
- Check expiration dates.
- Use ready-to-eat foods as soon as possible.
- Check canned goods for damage.
- Keep appliances at the proper temperatures.
- Clean the refrigerator regularly, and wipe up spills immediately.
- Avoid cross-contamination (which can occur when bacteria is spread from one food to another).

- Keep foods covered.
- Be alert to spoiled foods (look, smell, taste).
- Place food in the refrigerator when marinating.
- Don't store food under the sink.

PART I
PURCHASING YOUR FOOD

Safely Selecting and Transporting Food Products

The first step towards ensuring safe food begins at the grocery store. Checking product expiration, "best by," and "sell by" dates is essential for avoiding foodborne illness as well as food waste. Properly bagging your purchases and carefully transporting them home also will help ensure safe and healthy meals.

Understanding Product Dating

Experts estimate that $165 billion in food in the United States is thrown away each year as a result of fear generated by product expiration dates. This represents approximately 30 percent of the U.S. food supply. Many consumers think that expiration dates are tied to how safe food is to consume; however, these dates are not related to food safety or increasing the risk of foodborne illness. The only exception is infant formula and baby food, which the USDA advises parents not to buy or use if it is past the "use by" date.

Examples of expiration dates include: "Use By," "Best By," "Best Before," and "Best If Used By." These dates are normally found on shelf-stable foods. They are created by manufacturers to provide a guideline for optimal flavor and quality. These dates do not indicate spoilage, nor do they necessarily suggest that the food is no longer safe to eat. Therefore, it is usually okay to consume shelf-stable food beyond the expiration date. For example, dry pasta will most likely taste the same a year after the expiration date. The best way to determine if unopened shelf-stable products that are beyond the expiration date are still of good quality is to smell them and examine them. Foods can develop an off odor, flavor, or appearance due to spoilage bacteria. If a food has developed such characteristics, you should not use it for quality reasons. Remember, **when in doubt, throw it out**!

Adhering to these general food-dating guidelines does not guarantee consumers protection from foodborne illness. According to the USDA, bacteria can grow and lead to food-borne illness before and after the expiration date if food is not properly stored and handled.

Perishable and Nonperishable Foods

Foods are either *perishable or nonperishable*. Close attention should be paid to expiration dates on foods that are perish-able, as late-origin consumption is attributed to the most prevalent cases of food poisoning. Foods with a low-acid and high-moisture content are *perishable* and include dairy, meat, fish, poultry, fruits, and vegetables.

All other foods are *nonperishable* and are sometimes called *shelf-stable*. Dates on nonperishable foods are not related to quality but instead are used to indicate peak freshness. This helps store managers know how long to keep these items on shelves and to ensure the product is consumed before losing its flavor, nutrients, and consistency/texture. Therefore, dates on *nonperishable* foods are more a matter of ensuring optimal taste.

Though food product dating is not federally regulated, more than 20 states require food product dating – especially for *perishable* foods. However, with the exception of baby food and infant formula, there are areas of the U.S. where food is often not dated.

The Difference Between Open Dating
and Closed or Coded Dating

Open Dating "Open dating" refers to the use of a calendar date (11/1/17) as opposed to a code (1017-84BGD) or "closed date." Open dating appears primarily on perishable foods such as meat, poultry, eggs, and dairy products.

Closed or Coded Date This is a date coded by the manufacturers to track products, rotate stock, and determine when and where products were packaged, as well as enable the manufacturer to recall products, if needed. It would typically appear on shelf-stable products, such as canned or boxed foods, and does not indicate freshness or food quality.

Changing Dates It is legal for U.S. retailers to sell fresh or processed poultry and meat products past the package expiration date provided that the product is wholesome (not combined with other types of meat). Retailers also may legally change the date on fresh, wholesome meat that was cut and packaged in the store's meat department. It is not legal, however, to make changes to a label on any product that was packed under federal inspection. A product packaged under federal inspection may still be offered for sale, even with an expired date, as long as the food remains wholesome, but the expired date on the package may not be altered in any way or covered over with a different date.

Florida has specific practices pertaining to milk products. The shelf-removal date on milk products in the state of Florida can be no more than 10 days after the actual plant processing date. The product must be of a quality that permits it to be good for at least four and as many as seven days after the shelf-removal date. For example, milk processed in Florida on November 1 will have a shelf-removal date of November 11. The milk should then be of good quality for up to five days beyond the shelf-removal date, provided the product has been stored at 40°F or below. Use this information when deciding whether to throw out dairy products that have been in the refrigerator past the shelf-removal date.

Keep in mind that the length of time a product remains good varies from product to product. The temperature of the various storage and transportation environments (delivery truck, grocery store, car, etc.) affects the quality of the product and plays a role in determining how long after the shelf-removal date a product remains suitable for consumption. In short, the colder the temperature, the longer the product will retain freshness. For more information on this, see the "Food Storage and Longevity Charts."

Egg Carton Dating The use of a "Sell By" or "Expiration" date on egg cartons is not federally required but may be necessary depending on the state where the eggs are sold. Cartons displaying the USDA Grade shield must show the "pack date" (when the eggs were washed, graded, and packed in the carton). This date appears as a three-digit code representing the day of the year, beginning with 001 (Jan. 1) and ending with 365 (Dec. 31). If a "Sell By" date is stamped on an egg carton with a USDA Grade shield, that date may not extend beyond 45 days of the pack date.

Eggs should always be purchased before the "Expiration" or "Sell By" date displayed on the carton and refrigerated in their original package in the coldest part of the refrigerator (not in the door) as soon as they arrive home. To ensure the best quality, consume eggs within three to five weeks of the date of purchase. The "Sell By" date will usually elapse within that period of time.

Baby Food Federal regulation requires that all infant formula and many baby food products carry a "Use By" date. Dating of baby food is for quality as well as for nutrient retention. Infant formula and/or baby food should not be used past the "Use By" date.

Product Dating in General

Take time to check the date on the products you select. This will help ensure that you are purchasing wholesome and good-tasting food. While grocery stores strive to remove products that are outdated, it is up to you to make sure you don't purchase outdated food.

- The date should always be checked before a food product is purchased or consumed.
- Only purchase products that you plan to use before the "Use By" date.
- Questions about the date on a food product should be directed to a grocery store manager.
- Nonperishable foods can be safely consumed beyond the "Use By" date; however, the quality and taste may be somewhat compromised.
- If there is any question about the safety of a product, it should be thrown out!

Filling the Shopping Cart

Using a common sense approach to navigating the grocery store is key. For example, loading refrigerator, freezer, and hot-cooked items into the cart last will help prevent them from entering the temperature Danger Zone (between 40°-140°F). Also, pay close attention to the condition of packaging to avoid potentially contaminated or damaged products.

Egg Safety

Choose only refrigerated eggs, and make sure they are clean and in good shape. Open the carton to see if any of the eggs are cracked. If cracked eggs are found, select another carton that contains all uncracked eggs. Bacteria from a cracked egg can be transferred to the surface of a neighboring uncracked egg and then inside the uncracked egg, where bacteria can grow if the eggs are not properly refrigerated.

Egg Classification

There are a number of options to choose from when purchasing eggs, and egg carton labels can become a bit confusing. The following information, explaining the most common classifications of eggs available to consumers, is largely excerpted from the "egg-cyclopedia" at incredibleegg.org.

Conventional (no special labeling) Eggs laid by hens living in cages with access to feed, water, and shelter. The cages serve as nesting space as well as for production efficiency. In this type of hen house, the birds are more readily protected from the elements, from disease, and from natural and unnatural predators.

Cage-free Eggs laid by hens at indoor floor operations, sometimes also called free-roaming. The hens may roam in a building, room, or open area, usually in a barn or poultry house, and have unlimited access to fresh food and water, while some may also forage for food if they are allowed outdoors. Cage-free systems vary and include barn-raised and free-range hens, both of which have shelter that helps protect against predators. Both types are produced under common handling and care practices, which provide floor space, nest space, and perches. Depending on the farm, these housing systems may or may not have an automated egg-collection system.

Free-range Eggs produced by hens that have access to outdoors in accordance with weather and environmental or state laws. In addition to consuming a diet of grains, these hens may forage for wild plants and insects. When in cage-free indoor enclosures, they are provided floor space, nesting space, and perches.

Organic Eggs produced according to national USDA organic standards related to methods, practices, and substances used in producing and handling crops, livestock, and pro-cessed agricultural products. Organic eggs are produced by hens fed rations having ingredients that were grown with-out most conventional pesticides, fungicides, herbicides, or commercial fertilizers. All organic eggs are free-range eggs and must meet all of the requirements for those. The USDA inspects the farms before they are allowed to use the "organic label." Due to higher production costs, lower volume per farm, and certification costs, organic eggs are more expensive than eggs from hens fed conventional feed. The nutrient content of eggs is not affected by whether or not the feed ration is organic.

Enriched Colony A production system that contains ade-quate environmental enrichments to provide perch space, dust bathing, or scratch areas, and nest space to allow the layers to exhibit inherent behavior. Enriched colony systems are American Humane Certified.

Pasture-raised Eggs laid by hens that spend their days outside on fresh pastures rather than confined to cages or cage-free barns. Each bird is allotted 108 square feet of space where it can forage for grass and insects, living a life as close to natural as possible. Although some farms may claim pasture-raising, without the Certified Humane shield and the measure of space that's required to carry that shield, it's not true pasture-raising.

Vegetarian Eggs produced by hens fed a vegetarian diet with no animal byproducts.

White vs. brown eggs Simply put, the breed of hen determines the color of the egg's shell. Among commercial breeds, hens with white feathers and white ear lobes lay white-shelled eggs; hens with red feathers and red ear lobes lay brown eggs. Since brown-egg layers are slightly larger birds and require more food, brown eggs are usually more expensive than white. However, quality, flavor, and nutrition are not affected.

Omega-3 According to Consumer Reports, this designation indicates that hens were given feed that included flax, marine algae, fish oils, and other ingredients to boost the level of omega-3 fatty acid in their eggs.

Beware of the following label wordings that are basically empty claims:

Natural According to the USDA, this term simply means that nothing was added to the egg. All eggs meet this criterion.

Hormone-free, antibiotic-free No hormones or antibiotics are used in producing eggs for human consumption. Federal regulations prohibit the feeding of hormones to any kind of poultry in the U.S. Antibiotics are only rarely used when chickens are ill, at which time they seldom lay eggs. If antibiotics are used, FDA regulations require a withdrawal period for laying hens to ensure eggs are free of antibiotics.

Fruits and Vegetables

It is important to be selective when choosing fresh produce since many fruits and vegetables are highly perishable with a limited shelf life. Here are a few basic guidelines:

- Select the best-looking and freshest-smelling fruits and vegetables whenever possible.
- Always handle fruits and vegetables carefully. Although some items, such as cauliflower, may seem hardy, they actually are very delicate and may bruise easily.
- Ask your grocery store produce manager if you have a question about the quality of a fruit or vegetable.
- Never purchase fruits or vegetables that are bruised, shriveled, moldy, slimy, or have soft or brown spots. Also avoid fruits and vegetables that show signs of punctures or pest damage, have a foul smell, or contain a lot of liquid in the package (for some fruits, such as precut pineapple, it is okay to have liquid in the package). Attached leaves should not be wilted, and the color and texture of the produce should be appropriate for the type.
- It is not wise to "stock up" on fruits and vegetables. In most cases, they do not have a very long shelf life (exceptions include apples, citrus fruit, and potatoes).
- Don't get too caught up with tiny blemishes. Be smart; try to avoid unnecessary food waste.

Quality Grades for Fresh Fruits and Vegetables As a basis for trade, growers, shippers, wholesalers, and retailers make extensive use of the grade standards established for fresh fruits and vegetables by the U.S. Department of Agriculture (USDA). To a limited extent, these grade standards also are used in sales from retailers to consumers.

Although certain state laws and federal marketing programs require that certain fruits and vegetables be graded and labeled, the use of U.S. grade standards is voluntary. Packages of apples, pears, potatoes, and onions most often carry grade designations. Occasionally, other fruits and vegetables display grade designations.

The majority of fruit and vegetable packers grade their products, some even marking their packages with the grade. Note that if a package displays a grade, the packer is required under law to ensure that the product measures up to official grade requirements.

Below are the four grade designations for fruits and vegetables established by the USDA:

- **U.S. Fancy**: Premium quality, uniform shape, few defects. Only a small percentage of fruits and vegetables are packed in this grade.
- **U.S. No. 1**: Good quality, tender, fresh, free from bruises. This is the most commonly used grade for most fruits and vegetables.
- **U.S. No. 2**: Middle of the road; not as good as U.S. No. 1, but superior to U.S. No. 3.
- **U.S. No. 3**: The lowest grade practical to pack under normal commercial conditions. Still nutritious, but the appearance may not be as good as other grades.

Meat, Fish, Poultry, or Dairy

Consuming any meat, fish, poultry or dairy products that are less than fresh and wholesome can have potentially dangerous outcomes. Important information you should know when making your selections includes:

- Prevent cross-contamination, which occurs when harmful germs, like bacteria, get transferred from raw animal products to uncooked foods, such as fruits and vegetables. To prevent cross-contamination and foodborne illness, place raw seafood, meat, and poultry in plastic bags and keep them separated from other foods, either at the opposite end or underneath the shopping cart. This will help prevent their juices from dripping onto uncooked foods.
- Never select meat, fish, poultry or dairy products that feel warm to the touch or have a damaged or torn package. Place leaking packages in plastic bags.
- Select only pasteurized dairy products (milk, cheese, sour cream, yogurt, etc.). The pasteurization process ensures that no harmful bacteria will be present.
- Check the "use by" and "sell by" dates on all packages. Select packages with the most shelf life remaining.

Refrigerated, Frozen, and Hot Deli Foods

It is critical to ensure that hot and cold foods are not in the Danger Zone (between 40°-140°F) for more than two hours. Therefore, use the strategic approaches listed below when shopping for these items.

- Shop for refrigerated foods, frozen foods, and hot deli items last. Always keep cold foods cold (40°F or below)

and hot foods hot (140°F or above).
- Select only frozen food products that are frozen solid.

Shelf-Stable Foods

While these products offer greater longevity than other food items, there are still a number of things to consider when making your selections.

- Shop for shelf-stable foods (items stored in the pantry and cupboards) first.
- Purchase only cans that are in good condition. Never purchase cans that are swollen, bulging, leaking, or dented. Big dents can bend the metal, cause cracks in the can, and allow bacteria to get inside and grow.
- Always select cans and packages that appear to be new. Dusty cans and torn labels may indicate old stock.

Organic Foods

Previously only found at health food stores, organic foods are becoming increasingly available at local supermarkets. But what exactly qualifies food to be labeled "organic"? For meat, poultry, eggs, and dairy products to be considered organic, they must come from animals raised without the use of antibiotics or growth hormones; organic fruits and vegetables are grown without the use of chemical pesticides or irradiation. A government-approved certifier must inspect the farm where the food is grown in order to ensure total compliance with USDA organic standards before the food can be labeled organic.

Organic foods should be handled the same as non-organic foods. Organic foods are just as susceptible to microbial contamination as non-organic foods.

Bagging It

The next step toward ensuring your food's safety comes at the checkout counter. Proper packing of items is essential in maintaining their integrity.

- Always bag meats, fish, and poultry in a separate bag away from other foods.
- Bag cold and frozen items together. This will help maintain their proper temperature.
- Separate nonfood products, such as cleaning solutions, detergents, soaps, shampoo, lighter fluid, and charcoal, from food products.

Loading the Car and the Ride Home

Since cold foods need to remain at a temperature of 40°F or below, they should be placed in the coldest part of the car (normally the back seat with the air conditioning on during the summer and the trunk during the winter).

Grocery shopping should always be the last stop on a person's list of errands, and perishable items should be put away within 30 minutes of leaving the grocery store. If this is not possible, a cooler with ice should be used to store perishable items during the ride home.

PART II
AN "A TO Z" GUIDE TO FRESH FRUITS AND VEGETABLES

Fruits
Vegetables

An "A to Z" Guide
to Fresh Fruits and Vegetables

These charts provide information about where to store your food and how long it will remain fresh and maintain ideal quality. The longevity of food is determined by several factors including origination, transportation, storage locations, and storage temperatures. These charts should be used only as a guide. Remember, **when in doubt, throw it out!**

Much of the information in the "A to Z" Guide comes from the Food Keeper consumer brochure with permission from the Food Marketing Institute. This brochure was developed by the Food Marketing Institute with the Cornell University Institute of Food Science, the USDA's Meat and Poultry Hotline, and the FDA's Center for Food Safety and Applied Nutrition.

Fruits	
Acai Berries	
Selection:	Deep purple color
Storage location:	Freezer (as puree only)
Storage length:	5 years
Availability:	Fresh fruit not easily accessible and highly perishable; once harvested must be eaten or transported to processing unit

Apples

Selection:	Firm, crisp, well-colored, no bruises or soft spots
Storage location:	Shelf, refrigerator, or freezer
Storage length:	Shelf: 1-2 days
	Refrigerator: 3 weeks
	Freezer: 8 months
Availability:	Year-round

Apricots

Selection:	Plump, firm but not hard, golden-yellow color
Storage location:	Shelf or refrigerator
Storage length:	Shelf: Until ripe
	Refrigerator: 2-3 days
How to ripen:	Keep in a paper bag in a dark, cool place for 2 to 3 days. Avoid letting the apricots touch each other.
Availability:	June to July

Avocados

Selection:	Skin green to almost black, thin (California) or thick (Florida), smooth or rough, round or oblong, fresh-looking, firm but not hard
Storage location:	Shelf or refrigerator

Storage length:	Shelf: Until ripe Refrigerator: 3-4 days (skin will blacken)
How to ripen:	Place in a brown paper bag and store at room temperature; the process can be accelerated by adding a banana or an apple to the bag.
Availability:	January to April (California), July to January (Florida)

Bananas

Selection:	Firm, bright in appearance, free from bruises and brown spots
Storage location:	Shelf, refrigerator, or freezer
Storage length:	Shelf: Until ripe Refrigerator: 2 days (only after banana is ripe, skin will turn brown) Freezer: 1 month (whole, peeled)
How to ripen:	Keep in temperatures between 60°F and 70°F to ripen. Higher temperatures cause bananas to ripen too rapidly. A banana is at its best eating quality when the solid yellow color is specked with brown.

Availability:	Year-round
Helpful tip:	Refrigeration turns banana skins black, but the quality of the fruit is not affected.

Berries (strawberries listed separately)

Selection:	Bright, clean, fresh appearance; solid and plump; no mold or wetness; no stems or caps (except strawberry, gooseberry, and currant)
Storage location:	Refrigerator or freezer
Storage length:	Refrigerator: 1-2 days Freezer: 4 months
Availability:	May to August (exact season varies by type)
Helpful tip:	Most berries are very fragile and must be inspected carefully when purchased.

Cantaloupe

Selection:	Stem gone; thick, coarse, and corky netting/veining; yellowish-buff, gray, or pale yellow color between netting
Storage location:	Shelf (uncut until ripe), refrigerator (cut when ripe), or freezer (melon balls)
Storage length:	Shelf: 1-2 days until ripe.

	Refrigerator: 3-4 days (for ripe or cut cantaloupes)
	Freezer: 1 month (melon balls)
How to ripen:	Leave at room temperature for 2 to 4 days to complete ripening. A ripe cantaloupe will have a yellowish cast under the netting, a pleasant aroma, and yield slightly to light thumb pressure on blossom end of the melon. Cut cantaloupe must be refrigerated.
Availability:	Year-round
Helpful tip:	If uncut (whole) cantaloupes are left at room temperature, they will soften and become juicier.

Carambola (Starfruit)

Selection:	Light green to yellow, smooth waxy surface
Storage location:	Shelf or refrigerator
Storage length:	Shelf: 2-3 days until ripe
	Refrigerator: 2 weeks
Availability:	Year-round
Helpful tip:	Buy green and wait for fruit to turn yellow; effective as a garnish.

Cherimoya

Selection:	Fresh, firm, medium size, greenish-yellow, conical shape
Storage location:	Shelf or freezer (pureed or juiced)
Storage length:	Shelf: until ripe Freezer: several weeks
How to ripen:	To accelerate ripening, place in a paper bag and set in a warm spot, like on top of the refrigerator.
Availability:	October

Cherries

Selection:	Bright; plump; good color for type; firm but not hard, juicy, or dry
Storage location:	Refrigerator or freezer
Storage length:	Refrigerator: 1-2 days Freezer: 4 months
How to ripen:	If cherries have not reached mature size and full color, set on kitchen counter or place in a paper bag.
Availability:	Year-round

Coconuts, Fresh

Selection:	Heavy for size; no cracks; no indents that are damp, moist or moldy; should slosh with liquid and sound full when shaken
Storage location:	Shelf, refrigerator, or freezer
Storage length:	Shelf: 1 week opened; up to 4 months unopened at room temperature Refrigerator: 2-3 weeks opened; 4 days if grated; store in a tightly sealed container Freezer: 6 months if opened or shredded only
Availability:	Year-round; peak from October to December

Dates

Selection:	Oval to cylindrical; golden-yellow, amber, bright red, or brown
Storage location:	Shelf (in airtight container), refrigerator, or freezer (tightly wrapped)
Storage length:	Shelf: 4 weeks Refrigerator: 6-12 months Freezer: 1 year

Availability:	September to March
Helpful tip:	Avoid dates with crystalized sugars.

Dragon Fruit (Pitaya)

Selection:	Bright, even-colored skin; usually dark red in color; not too soft or mushy; blotches may indicate fruit is overripe
Storage location:	Refrigerator (uncut in paper bag) or freezer (as pulp)
Storage length:	Refrigerator: 3 months Freezer: 3 months
How to ripen:	If very firm, ripen for a few days at room temperature.
Availability:	Summer and early fall
Helpful tip:	Its flavor is a cross between kiwi and pear.

Durian

Selection:	Firm stalk, light-colored spikes with no dark brown patches or white between spikes
Storage location:	Shelf, refrigerator, or freezer
Storage length:	Shelf: 2-3 days Refrigerator: several days Freezer: 3 months
How to ripen:	The fruit is unripe if it has no

odor. To ripen, store in a warm place in an airtight container.

Availability:	Year-round frozen
Helpful tip:	Has a naturally very strong, unpleasant odor.

Figs, Fresh

Selection:	Clean and dry with smooth, unbroken skin; soft and yielding to the touch but not mushy
Storage location:	Refrigerator (in plastic pouch) or freezer
Storage length:	Refrigerator: 2-3 days Freezer: 10-12 months
Availability:	May to December
Helpful tip:	Store in separate container away from vegetables; overripe figs will have a bad smell.

Grapefruit

Selection:	Firm; heavy for size; smooth, thin skin
Storage location:	Shelf (if using within 1 week) or refrigerator (if keeping more than 1 week)
Storage length:	Shelf: 7-10 days Refrigerator: 1-2 weeks
Availability:	Year-round; peak from

	November to May
Helpful tip:	Pink grapefruit is generally sweeter than white varieties.

Grapes

Selection:	Well-colored, plump, firmly attached to stem, no brittle or dry stems
Storage location:	Shelf, refrigerator (unwashed in a plastic bag), or freezer (whole)
Storage length:	Shelf: 1 day Refrigerator: 1 week Freezer: 1 month
Availability:	Year-round
Helpful tip:	Grapes do not ripen after they are picked. Do not get them wet; wash them just before serving.

Guava

Selection:	Medium firm and fragrant, bright green to light yellow
Storage location:	Shelf, refrigerator (when ripe), or freezer (as puree)
Storage length:	Shelf: 2-5 days (or until ripe) Refrigerator: 3-4 days Freezer: 10-12 months
How to ripen:	Keep in a paper bag with an

	apple at room temperature.
Availability:	Year-round
Helpful tip:	May be eaten fresh or used to make preserves.

Honeydew Melon

Selection:	Soft, velvety texture; slight softening at blossom end; pleasant aroma; yellowish-white to creamy rind color
Storage location:	Shelf (uncut until ripe), refrigerator (cut when ripe), or freezer (melon balls)
Storage length:	Shelf: 1-2 days Refrigerator: 3-4 days Freezer: 1 month
How to ripen:	Place in a paper bag with an apple until ripe; a hollow sound when the melon is thumped and a sweet aroma indicate ripeness.
Availability:	Year-round; peak from June to September

Kiwifruits

Selection:	Firm; plump; fuzzy light-brown skin that gives slightly to the touch
Storage location:	Shelf or refrigerator

Storage length:	Shelf: Until ripe
	Refrigerator: 3-4 days (ripe
	kiwi only)
How to ripen:	Ripen at room temperature,
	or place in a paper bag with
	an apple or banana or in a
	ripening bowl to speed up
	ripening process.
Availability:	Year-round
Helpful tip:	The skin is edible, but the
	fruit is usually served peeled.

Kumquats

Selection:	Firm, smooth, bright orange
	color with attached stem
Storage location:	Shelf, refrigerator, or freezer
	(as puree)
Storage length:	Shelf: 3-4 days
	Refrigerator: 3 weeks
	Freezer: 6 months
How to ripen:	If the skin is still a bit green,
	the fruit will ripen at room
	temperature.
Availability:	January to September
Helpful tip:	The skin is edible.

Lemons

Selection:	Rich yellow color, reasonably smooth skin with a slight gloss, firm, and heavy
Storage location:	Shelf (for short term) or refrigerator (for long term)
Storage length:	Shelf: 7-10 days Refrigerator: 1-2 weeks
Availability:	Year-round
Helpful tip:	To release more juice, microwave the lemon for 10 seconds before cutting.

Limes

Selection:	Smooth, plump skin; heavy for size; uniform deep-green or yellow-green color
Storage location:	Shelf or refrigerator
Storage length:	Shelf: 7-10 days Refrigerator: 1-2 weeks
Availability:	Year-round

Lychees

Selection:	Short piece of stem attached to fruit; avoid if dark brown (overripe)
Storage location:	Shelf, refrigerator, or freezer
Storage length:	Shelf: 2-3 days

	Refrigerator: 5 weeks
	Freezer: several weeks
Availability:	May to October

Mangos

Selection:	Red, green, yellow, orange, or a combination of colors; firm to fairly soft; bumpy, slightly rough skin
Storage location:	Shelf or refrigerator
Storage length:	Shelf: 3-5 days
	Refrigerator: 1 week
How to ripen:	Place in a paper bag (do not close the bag completely), wrap in newspaper at room temperature, or submerge in a bowl of uncooked rice or popcorn kernels. Mangos are ripe when they give off a heavy, fruity odor and are soft to the touch.
Availability:	May to August

Mangosteen

Selection:	Bright purple, feels heavy in hand, firm green calyx
Storage location:	Refrigerator
Storage length:	2 weeks
Availability:	June to October

Nectarines

Selection:	Firm but not hard, plump, yellow-orange skin with red blush, fragrant
Storage location:	Shelf, refrigerator, or freezer
Storage length:	Shelf: Until ripe
	Refrigerator: 3-4 days
	Freezer: 2 months, when sliced with lemon juice and sugar
How to ripen:	Keep at room temperature in a paper bag until the fruit gives to gentle pressure along the seam. Do not store nectarines in plastic bags, and don't put them in the sun as they won't ripen properly.
Availability:	June to August

Oranges

Selection:	Firm, heavy for size, fine-textured skin, well-colored, thick skin for navel oranges, thin skin for juice oranges
Storage location:	Shelf or refrigerator
Storage length:	Shelf: 10 days
	Refrigerator: 1-2 weeks
Availability:	Year-round
Helpful tip:	Thin-skinned oranges are

ideal for juicing. Thick-skinned and blood oranges (with red pulp), including the navel (which is large, seedless and easy to peel), make the best eating oranges.

Papayas

Selection:	Smooth, thin skin; changes from green to red or orange when ripe; soft
Storage location:	Shelf or refrigerator
Storage length:	Shelf: 3-5 days
	Refrigerator: 1 week
How to ripen:	Ripen at room temperature for several days.
Availability:	Year-round

Passionfruit (Granadilla)

Selection:	Golden yellow or purple, plump, heavy for size, well ripened
Storage location:	Shelf, refrigerator, or freezer
Storage length:	Shelf: 1-2 days
	Refrigerator: 1 week
	Freezer: 6-8 months
How to ripen:	Leave on the counter for one to two days to fully ripen, until the skin turns yellow

	and the tips of the ribs turn brown. Turn the fruit every 12 hours during ripening.
Availability:	Year-round
Helpful tip:	Purple type is less acid than yellow.

Peaches

Selection:	Fairly firm and a little soft, plump, should give a bit when squeezed in the palm of the hand, creamy yellow color between the red areas; mature peaches have no tinge of green in the lighter part of the skin
Storage location:	Shelf, refrigerator, or freezer
Storage length:	Shelf: Until ripe
	Refrigerator: 3-4 days (when ripe)
	Freezer: 2 months, when sliced with lemon juice and sugar
How to ripen:	Store in ripening bowl or paper bag to soften; they will get juicier but not sweeter.
Availability:	Most of the year; peak from late April to October
Helpful tip:	All peaches fall into two categories: clingstones and

freestones. Clingstones have flesh that clings to the pit, whereas the flesh of a freestone separates easily.

Pears

Selection:	Firm but not hard, no blemishes
Storage location:	Shelf or refrigerator
Storage length:	Shelf: 3-5 days Refrigerator: 3-4 days
How to ripen:	Pears ripen best between 65°F and 75°F. The fruit is ripe when the flesh near the stem is slightly soft. Putting a banana or ripe apple in with the fruit helps to speed up ripening.
Availability:	Year-round
Helpful tip:	Pears are usually picked for shipping before they have ripened. It is difficult to find a perfectly ripe pear in the market. The flesh of pears is extremely fragile.

Pineapples

Selection:	Bright, fragrant aroma; slight separation of the eyes or pips;

	firm; plump; heavy for size
Storage location:	Shelf or refrigerator
Storage length:	Shelf: 1-2 days
	Refrigerator: 1-7 days
How to ripen:	Store at room temperature for 2-3 days to ripen.
Availability:	Year-round
Helpful tip:	When mature, pineapples are usually dark green, firm, plump, and heavy for size.

Plums

Selection:	Various shades of red, purple, and green; plump and firm to slightly soft; no cuts, bruises, sunburn, or stickiness
Storage location:	Shelf or refrigerator
Storage length:	Shelf: 3-5 days
	Refrigerator: 3-4 days
How to ripen:	Plums ripen quickly at temperatures between 68°F and 77°F. Ripe fruit yields to gentle pressure and are sweeter, softer, and more prone to bruising.
Availability:	May to September
Helpful tip:	Store at room temperature until ripe, then refrigerate in plastic bag.

Pomegranates

Selection:	Plump, round, distinctive color, smooth skin, free from bruises
Storage location:	Shelf or refrigerator
Storage length:	Shelf: 5-8 days
	Refrigerator: 2-3 weeks
Availability:	September to February

Quinces

Selection:	Well-developed, firm, bright golden color
Storage location:	Shelf, refrigerator, or freezer
Storage length:	Shelf: 2-5 days
	Refrigerator: 2-3 weeks
	Freezer: 2 months
How to ripen:	Place in a dry, cool location out of direct sunlight for a few days, turning several times. For a greener quince that needs longer ripening, enclose in a plastic bag or container and store in a cool place for 1 to 2 months.
Availability:	September to January
Helpful tip:	High in tannins, which help to tenderize meat.

Sapodilla

Selection:	Grey/brown "kiwifruit like" outer surface, smooth, no wrinkles
Storage location:	Shelf, refrigerator, or freezer
Storage length:	Shelf: 7-10 days Refrigerator: 2-3 weeks Freezer: 1 month
How to ripen:	Place on the kitchen counter or in a paper bag to ripen more quickly (it will usually take about 3 to 5 days). Sapodillas are ripe when they are soft and have a sweet aroma.
Availability:	May to September
Helpful tip:	Wash off before putting aside to ripen; can take up to 9 days to ripen.

Strawberries

Selection:	Firm flesh, full red color, bright luster, cap stem still attached, no mold
Storage location:	Refrigerator or freezer
Storage length:	Refrigerator: 1-2 days (unwashed) Freezer: 4 months
Availability:	Year-round; peak from April to August

| Helpful tip: | Only wash strawberries right before serving them. Strawberries do not ripen after they are picked. |

Tangerines

Selection:	Deep yellow or orange color, bright luster, puffy, and loose skin
Storage location:	Shelf or refrigerator
Storage length:	Shelf: 10 days
	Refrigerator: 1-2 weeks
Availability:	October to May

Watermelons

Selection:	Cut: Firm, juicy flesh with good red color; dark brown or black seeds; free from white streaks
	Whole: Relatively smooth surface, slight dullness at rind, filled-out and rounded ends, creamy color on underside
Storage location:	Shelf (uncut until ripe), refrigerator (cut when ripe), or freezer (melon balls)
Storage length:	Shelf: 1-2 days
	Refrigerator: 3-4 days

	Freezer: 1 month
How to ripen:	Store in a closed paper bag at room temperature for 3 to 4 days. Tap the watermelon lightly; a dull thud indicates the watermelon is ripe.
Availability:	May to August

Vegetables

Artichokes, Whole

Selection:	Globe trimmed; well-formed, plump, clinging, fleshy leaf scales of good, uniform, bright, dark-green color
Storage location:	Shelf or refrigerator
Storage length:	Shelf: 1-2 days
	Refrigerator: 1-2 weeks (raw)
Availability:	March to May and November to December
Helpful tip:	Sprinkle with water before storing.

Asparagus

Selection:	Fresh, tender, firm, fairly straight stalks with close compact tips

Storage location:	Refrigerator (wrap the aspar-agus stem ends in a wet paper towel and put them in a plastic bag, or stand them up with the stems in a little water) or freezer (blanched or cooked)
Storage length:	Refrigerator: 3-4 days Freezer: 8 months
Availability:	August to June; peak from April to May
Helpful tip:	Use quickly; there is no benefit from storage.

Beans, Green/Snap/Wax

Selection:	Bright green, clean, fresh, tender, firm, long, straight, should snap when bent
Storage location:	Refrigerator (unwashed in plastic bag) or freezer (blanched or cooked)
Storage length:	Refrigerator: 3-4 days Freezer: 8 months
Availability:	Year-round

Beets

| Selection: | Smooth, free of blemishes, no deep cuts or leaf scars around top, no soft spots, |

	globe-shaped
Storage location:	Shelf, refrigerator, or freezer (blanched or cooked)
Storage length:	Shelf: 1 day
	Refrigerator: 7-10 days
	Freezer: 6-8 months
Availability:	June to October; peak in July
Helpful tip:	Remove tops before storing

Bok Choy

Selection:	Wide stalks with vivid green leaves, no blemishes or gouges
Storage location:	Refrigerator (unwashed in plastic bag) or freezer
Storage length:	Refrigerator: 2-3 days
	Freezer: 10-12 months
Availability:	Year-round
Helpful tip:	Chop an inch off the stalk before washing.

Broccoli

Selection:	Green flower, not yellow; tender, firm stalks; compact buds; 6"–8" long
Storage location:	Refrigerator (unwashed in a plastic bag in the crisper) or freezer
Storage length:	Refrigerator: 3 days

| | Freezer: 10-12 months |
| Availability: | Year-round |

Brussels Sprouts

Selection:	Compact; bright green; firm; not withered, puffy, or burst
Storage location:	Refrigerator (in crisper) or freezer
Storage length:	Refrigerator: 3-5 days Freezer: 10-12 months
Availability:	January to May

Cabbage, Green/Red

Selection:	Firm, heavy for size, no discolored veins, no decayed or burst heads
Storage location	Refrigerator (unwashed in plastic bag in crisper) or freezer (blanched or cooked)
Storage length:	Refrigerator: 1-2 weeks Freezer: 10-12 months
Availability:	Year-round

Carrots

| Selection: | Firm; clean; fresh-looking; smooth; well-shaped; good orange color; not split, wilted, flabby, soft, or shriveled |

Storage location:	Refrigerator (unwashed, without green tops, in a plastic bag) or freezer (blanched or cooked)
Storage length:	Refrigerator: 4 weeks (mature, raw); 2 weeks (young, peeled); see "best before" date for baby carrots Freezer: 10-12 months
Availability:	Year-round
Helpful tip:	Remove tops before storing.

Cauliflower

Selection:	White or creamy white, clean, heavy, firm, compact curd, no heavy spreading of flower clusters
Storage location:	Refrigerator (unwashed, in plastic bag, in the crisper) or freezer
Storage length:	Refrigerator: 2 weeks Freezer: 10-12 months
Availability:	Year-round; peak from September to November
Helpful tip:	Old cauliflower gives off a strong taste and smell.

Celery

Selection:	Medium length, thickness,

	and solidity; stalks brittle, not stringy, fairly straight; outer stalks light green to green; no black heart or excessive growth of heart
Storage location:	Refrigerator (in a plastic container, sprinkle with water to retard wilting) or freezer (blanched or cooked)
Storage length:	Refrigerator: 1-2 weeks Freezer: 10-12 months
Availability:	Year-round; peak from November to April

Cilantro

Selection:	Bright, evenly colored green leaves; no signs of wilting
Storage location:	Shelf (in glass of water), refrigerator, or freezer
Storage length:	Shelf: 1-3 days, Refrigerator: 1 week (depending on market treatment) Freezer: 1-2 months
Availability:	Year-round
Helpful tip:	Do not wash until ready to use.

Corn on the Cob

Selection:	Fresh, succulent, tightly

	wrapped green husk; bright, plump, firm, milky kernels; tassels brown and silky, not green
Storage location:	Refrigerator or freezer
Storage length:	Refrigerator: 1-2 days
	Freezer: 8 months
Availability:	Year-round; peak May to September

Cucumbers

Selection:	Firm, fresh, bright, well-shaped, good green color
Storage location:	Refrigerator (store cut and whole cucumbers in a plastic bag)
Storage length:	4-5 days
Availability:	Year-round

Eggplant

Selection:	Glossy; heavy for size; firm; smooth; free of blemishes; deep purple, creamy white, or speckled; light-brown seeds; flesh not brown
Storage location:	Shelf, refrigerator, or freezer (blanched or cooked)
Storage length:	Shelf: 1 day
	Refrigerator: 3-4 days

| | Freezer: 6-8 months |
| Availability: | August to September |

Garlic

Selection:	Firm, dry, plump cloves with outer skin or sheath intact and dry; minimum diameter 1" pink or white skin
Storage location:	Shelf, refrigerator, or freezer (blanched or cooked)
Storage length:	Shelf: 2 days Refrigerator: 1-2 weeks Freezer: 1 month
Availability:	Year-round

Ginger Root

Selection:	Smooth skin; fresh, spicy fragrance; should feel firm and heavy
Storage location:	Shelf, refrigerator, or freezer (blanched or cooked)
Storage length:	Shelf: 1-2 days Refrigerator: 1-3 weeks Freezer: 1-2 months
Availability:	Year-round
Helpful tip:	To use frozen ginger, slice off a piece of unthawed root; rewrap unused portion and return to freezer.

Greens, Leafy

Selection:	Fresh, firm, deep-green leaves, crisp, no discoloration
Storage location:	Refrigerator (wrap them in a damp paper towel and store in a perforated plastic bag; leafy greens need some moisture, but they do not need to be kept wet) or freezer
Storage length:	Refrigerator: 1-2 days Freezer: 10-12 months
Availability:	Year-round
Helpful tip:	Greens cook down considerably to one-quarter or less of their original volume.

Herbs, Fresh

Selection:	Good green color; good aroma; fresh-looking leaves and stems; no wilt, brown spots, sunburn, or pest damage
Storage location:	Refrigerator (wrap loosely in damp paper towel or cloth to reduce wilting of leaves and retain freshness; store wrapped herbs in plastic bag) or freezer
Storage length:	Refrigerator: 7-10 days

	Freezer: 1-2 months
Availability:	Year-round
Helpful tip:	The quality of both fresh and dried herbs can be best assessed by their aroma. You can test them by crumbling a few leaves between your fingers and then smelling the leaves.

Leeks

Selection:	Thick neck (1" in diameter), well-blanched, crisp, tender, fresh tops
Storage location:	Refrigerator or freezer (blanched or cooked)
Storage length:	Refrigerator: 1-2 weeks Freezer: 10-12 months
Availability:	Year-round

Lettuce, Iceberg

Selection:	Fresh, crisp, tender leaves; fairly firm head; heavy for size; no rot or decay; small core
Storage location:	Refrigerator (store in a tightly closed bag or container; store in crisper)
Storage length:	1-2 weeks
Availability:	Year-round

Lettuce, Leaf (includes several varieties)

Selection:	Broad, tender, succulent, and fairly smooth leaves; vary in color according to variety
Storage location:	Refrigerator (store in a tightly closed bag or container; store in crisper)
Storage length:	3-7 days
Availability:	Year-round

Lettuce, Packaged (prewashed and cut)

Selection:	Select package with the most shelf life remaining (see date stamped on package)
Storage location:	Refrigerator (store in a tightly closed bag or container; store in crisper)
Storage length:	Up to (and possibly a few days past) the date stamped on the package
Availability:	Year-round

Lettuce, Romaine

Selection:	Tall and cylindrical; crisp, dark-green leaves in a loosely folded head; tender, small heart
Storage location:	Refrigerator (store in a tightly

	closed bag or container; store in crisper)
Storage length:	3-7 days
Availability:	Year-round

Mushrooms

Selection:	Young; small to medium size; clean; dry; unblemished white, creamy, or tan cap; short stem; button mushrooms should have stem fully attached to cap; avoid wide-open caps and dark, discolored gills
Storage location:	Refrigerator (in a paper bag) or freezer (blanched or cooked)
Storage length:	Refrigerator: 2-3 days Freezer: 10-12 months
Availability:	Year-round
Helpful tip:	Wash mushrooms only right before use; store in a paper bag, not in a plastic bag. Mushrooms are highly perishable.

Okra

Selection:	Young, tender pods (not soft); under 4" long; free of bruises

Storage location:	Refrigerator (store in a paper bag or wrap in a paper towel and store in a perforated plastic bag) or freezer (blanched or cooked)
Storage length:	Refrigerator: 2-3 days Freezer: 10-12 months
Availability:	Year-round in the South, May to October in other areas

Onions, Dry (yellow, white, and red)

Selection:	Clean, hard, firm, and well-shaped; small necks; dry, brittle skin of appropriate color; no stems, wetness, or decay
Storage location:	Shelf (store in a cool, dry, dark place in a loosely woven bag, basket, or crate that has good air circulation), refrigerator or freezer (blanched or cooked)
Storage length:	Shelf: 2-3 weeks Refrigerator: 2 months Freezer: 10-12 months
Availability:	Year-round

Onions, Green (Scallions)

| Selection: | Fresh tops, minimum wilt, |

	medium-size necks, crisp
Storage location:	Refrigerator (unwashed) or freezer
Storage length:	Refrigerator: 1-2 weeks Freezer: 10-12 months
Availability:	Year-round
Helpful tip:	Use green onions as soon as possible as they are fairly per-ishable.

Parsley

Selection:	Deep green color, looks fresh and crisp, no wilted or yellow leaves
Storage location:	Refrigerator (in plastic bag) or freezer
Storage length:	Refrigerator: 1 week Freezer: 1-2 months
Availability:	Year-round

Parsnips

Selection:	Firm, smooth, well-shaped, no large side roots, small to medium size, may be wax-coated
Storage location:	Refrigerator or freezer (blanched or cooked)
Storage length:	Refrigerator: 2 weeks (see "best before" date)

| | Freezer: 10-12 months |
| Availability: | October to December |

Peppers, Bell/Chili

Selection:	Mature; firm; thick flesh; uniform color, size, and shape
Storage location:	Refrigerator (in plastic bag) or freezer (blanched or cooked)
Storage length:	Refrigerator: 4-5 days Freezer: 6-8 months
Availability:	Year-round

Potatoes

Selection:	Firm, smooth, clean, shallow eyes, no wet spots
Storage location:	Shelf (store in a paper bag in a cool, dry, dark place), refrigerator, or freezer (cooked and mashed)
Storage length:	Shelf: 1-2 months Refrigerator: 1-2 weeks Freezer: 10-12 months
Availability:	Year-round
Helpful tip:	Avoid storing potatoes in the refrigerator as this may alter the taste. Also, a bitter taste may be created when potatoes are stored in the light.

For best results, store potatoes in a paper bag in a dry,
cool place.

Potatoes, Sweet

Selection:	Smooth, well-shaped, bright orange color, no soft spots or blemishes
Storage location:	Shelf (store in a cool, dry storage bin) or refrigerator
Storage length:	Shelf: 2 weeks Refrigerator: 2-3 months
Availability:	Year-round
Helpful tip:	Sweet potatoes bruise and discolor easily; handle with care.

Radishes

Selection:	Well-shaped, smooth, firm, crisp-tender, even color (bright red, white), crisp tops
Storage location:	Refrigerator (sprinkle with water before storing)
Storage length:	2 weeks
Availability:	Year-round
Helpful tip:	Remove tops before storing.

Rutabagas

Selection:	Fairly smooth, no blemishes, light yellow to buff color
Storage location:	Shelf, refrigerator, or freezer (blanched or cooked)
Storage length:	Shelf: 1 week Refrigerator: 2 weeks Freezer: 8-10 months
Availability:	October to March

Spinach, Leaf

Selection:	Clean, fresh, crisp-tender, good color, flat, or curly
Storage location:	Refrigerator (rinse, drain, and refrigerate immediately in a tightly closed bag or container in crisper) or freezer (blanched or cooked)
Storage length:	Refrigerator: 1-2 days (raw) Freezer: 10-12 months
Availability:	Year-round

Squash, Summer

Selection:	Heavy for size, no blemishes or soft spots, tender rind (easily punctured), small
Storage location:	Refrigerator or freezer (blanched or cooked)

Storage length:	Refrigerator: 4-5 days
	Freezer: 10-12 months
Availability:	July to November
Helpful tip:	Rind and seeds are edible.

Squash, Winter

Selection:	Heavy for size; no blemishes, cracks or soft spots; hard rind
Storage location:	Shelf or refrigerator
Storage length:	Shelf: 1 week
	Refrigerator: 2 weeks
Availability:	July to November

Tomatoes

Selection:	Mature or vine-ripened; deep, even color; well-shaped; plump; smooth; no blemishes
Storage location:	Shelf (whole), refrigerator (cut), or freezer (blanched or cooked)
Storage length:	Shelf: until ripe
	Refrigerator: 2-3 days
	Freezer: 2 months
Availability:	Year-round
Helpful tip:	Cut tomatoes should be refrigerated even though refrigeration will alter the taste.

Turnips

Selection:	Medium size, smooth, firm, good color (white at tip, purple near top), few leaf scars around crown
Storage location:	Refrigerator or freezer (blanched or cooked)
Storage length:	Refrigerator: 2 weeks Freezer: 8-10 months
Availability:	October to March
Helpful tip:	Need to be scrubbed but not peeled before eating

PART III
STORING YOUR FOOD

Storing Food Products

The proper storage and packaging of groceries help prevent cross-contamination. In addition, this preserves the longevity and quality of food. Understanding the difference between perishable and nonperishable foods is critical to proper storage:

- Perishable foods include items susceptible to spoilage without proper refrigeration, such as meat, poultry, seafood, fresh vegetables, fresh fruits, eggs, and dairy products such as milk, sour cream, yogurt, and soft cheese.
- Nonperishable foods include foods that are shelf-stable—meaning they do not need to be refrigerated—such as canned goods, pasta, rice, cereal, flour, and peanut butter. Keep in mind that many of these items become perishable once they are opened, like pasta sauce and jarred vegetables.

Following a few basic principles will help ensure food's safety and maintain its value:

- Put cold items away first.
- Store meat separately.
- Wash hands after handling meat.
- Monitor your refrigerator frequently to ensure proper temperatures are maintained at 40°F or less.

Labeling all perishables as well as jarred items (jam, salsa, mayonnaise), boxed goods (cereal, crackers, pasta), and bottles (salad dressing, ketchup) upon opening makes it easy to determine the freshness of the contents in the future.

Perishable Foods

Perishable foods must be stored at a temperature of 40°F or below to limit bacteria from multiplying to dangerous levels, making food unsafe to eat.

Foods for Pregnant Women to Avoid During pregnancy, changes to the immune system can create greater vulnerability to foodborne illness. To be safe, certain types of foods should be avoided. Among the most common are:

- Foods prepared with raw eggs, such as homemade eggnog, raw cookie dough, and restaurant-prepared Caesar salad dressing, as well as any preparation of eggs in which both the yolk and white are not thoroughly cooked (for example, sunny-side up).
- Raw or undercooked meat, poultry, fish, and shellfish, as well as certain varieties of fish that contain high levels of mercury, including swordfish, grouper, tilefish, sea bass, albacore tuna, and yellowfin tuna. Examples of safer seafood choices are salmon, flounder, sole, haddock, shrimp, scallops, and canned light tuna.
- Unpasteurized milk and juice, such as might be sold at farm stands.
- Soft cheeses such as brie, feta, camembert, and queso blanco.
- Unwashed fresh fruits and vegetables, even if the skin will not be eaten. Note: Prebagged and prewashed leafy greens should always be rewashed to help remove microbial pathogens.
- Deli meat that has not been heated to steaming to kill any potential bacteria. Simple heating methods for deli sandwiches are grilling, toasting, and microwaving.

While cold temperatures keep food fresh and inhibit the growth of most bacteria, microorganisms causing food spoilage can still grow and multiply over time, even in a cold environment. As there is a LIMIT to the length of time foods will stay fresh in the refrigerator, labeling all perishables on the date they are opened will help determine food quality before consumption. Date labeling will also allow you to determine which products are oldest and should be consumed first. See the "How Long Foods Last" section of this book for more information and specific details on food longevity.

Meat, Poultry, and Seafood The coldest air circulates in the lowest part of the refrigerator. As meat, poultry, and seafood will remain fresh longer when stored at colder temperatures, all meats should be stored in the bin situated on the bottom shelf. Placing meat, poultry, and seafood in the bottom bin also prevents cross-contamination by containing any dripping juices and keeping them from coming in contact with ready-to-eat foods. Meat, poultry, and seafood should be left in their original packaging until food prep begins, as repeated handling could not only introduce bacteria into the meat but also spread bacteria around the kitchen. To further prevent leakage resulting in cross-contamination, place store-packaged meat in a leak-proof container to contain juices and keep meat fresh longer.

Dairy and Egg Products Dairy products include butter, cheese, milk, cream, dips, pudding, sour cream, and yogurt. Dairy and egg products should be stored on the refrigerator shelves in the original packaging and never in the door. The door is the warmest area in the refrigerator and should be used for storing condiments, nondairy drinks, jarred foods, etc. Cheeses will benefit from the high humidity levels in one of the mid-level crisper bins.

Fruits and Vegetables Not all fruits and vegetables require refrigeration. For a complete list of how and where to store fruits and vegetables, refer to "Food Storage and Longevity Charts" in this book.

- Put produce away promptly, and try to keep most of your fruits and vegetables in the crisper. The crisper has a higher humidity level than the rest of the refrigerator, which is better for fruits and vegetables and prevents them from quickly drying out. See the "Food Storage and Longevity Charts" section for the proper storage location of most fruits and vegetables.
- Never wash or rinse fruits and vegetables before you put them away (except for salad greens and fresh herbs, which should be washed before they are stored in the refrigerator), as moisture often causes some fruits and vegetables to spoil prematurely.
- Wash fruits and vegetables with warm water just before eating or cooking them. This applies even if you don't eat the skin, as with oranges and melons (when you cut into a fruit or vegetable, any bacteria on the outer surface can be transferred to the inner flesh).
- Never wash fruits and vegetables (or any food product) with detergent. Fruits and vegetables can absorb the detergent, which can make you sick.
- Remove the outer leaves before washing leafy vegetables, such as lettuce and cabbage.
- Scrub produce items like potatoes, carrots, and apples under warm water with a soft-bristled brush before they are eaten or cooked.

- Never keep fruits and vegetables in the refrigerator once they have spoiled.
- Store cut fruits and vegetables in the refrigerator in a zip-lock bag or sealed container, above raw meat, poultry, and fish, and below cooked items.

Storage Location for Fruits and Vegetables

Raw fruits and vegetables are safe to store at room temperature; however, after ripening, they will quickly mold and rot. For the best quality, store ripe fruits and vegetables in the refrigerator, or prepare and then freeze them. The exceptions to this rule are dense raw vegetables, such as onions, rutabagas, and potatoes. These products should be stored at cool room temperatures.

Most fruits and vegetables should be kept dry because moisture can promote spoilage. Produce should therefore not be peeled, washed, or trimmed until just before it is used. The outer leaves of lettuce, for example, should be left intact; carrots should remain unpeeled. Leafy tops on green vegetables like beets, carrots, radishes, and turnips should be removed; even after harvesting, the leaves absorb nutrients from the root and increase moisture loss.

After cooking, all fruits and vegetables must be refrigerated or frozen within two hours. Cooked fruits and vegetables must never be left in the Danger Zone (between 40°–140°F) for more than two hours.

How Ethylene Gas Affects Produce Ripening and Spoilage

Ethylene gas is a naturally occurring plant hormone produced by some fruits as they ripen. It is an invisible, odorless hydrocarbon gas that is not harmful to humans. In general, fruits and vegetables that continue to ripen after being picked are the ones that produce high levels of ethylene gas.

Storing ethylene-producing fruits and vegetables next to ethylene-sensitive produce may reduce shelf life and reduce the quality of certain items, leading to storage challenges and possibly causing premature spoiling and decay. Reducing exposure to ethylene slows down the natural ripening.

Here are a few tips to prevent quick spoilage and extend the life of your produce:

- Keep ethylene-sensitive produce away from ethylene-producing produce.
- Store vegetables away from fruits in the refrigerator.
- Fruits and vegetables that produce large amounts of ethylene gas should be left unwrapped or wrapped loosely so the gas can escape. This will slow the ripening process.
- Keep apples and bananas away from other produce (unless you want to speed up ripening).
- Other effects of ethylene gas on produce include spotting, yellowing, odor, wilting, and loss of crispness.

Listed below are ethylene-producing and ethylene-sensitive fruits and vegetables. (Note that some items are included on both lists.)

Ethylene Producers

Apples	Mangosteen
Apricots	Melons
Avocados	Nectarines
Bananas (ripe)	Papayas
Blueberries	Passion fruit
Cantaloupe	Peaches
Cranberries	Pears
Figs	Persimmons
Grapes	Plums
Green onions	Potatoes
Guava	Prunes
Kiwifruit	Quince
Mangos	Tomatoes

TIP: MAYONNAISE SAFETY

According to Hellmann's, mayonnaise is NOT a food safety problem! The ingredients in mayonnaise, such as vinegar, lemon juice, and salt, create an unfavorable environment for bacteria that will slow or prevent its growth. However, many of the ingredients typically mixed with mayonnaise, like potatoes, ham, or chicken, have a greater susceptibility to bacterial growth than the mayonnaise itself.

Ethylene-Sensitive Produce

Apples	Lettuce
Apricots	Nectarines
Asparagus	Okra
Avocados	Peaches
Bananas (unripe)	Pears
Blueberries	Peas
Broccoli	Peppers
Brussels sprouts	Spinach
Cabbage	Raspberries
Carrots	Strawberries
Cauliflower	Sweet potatoes/
Chard	Yams
Eggplant	Tomatoes
Garlic	Watercress
Green Beans	Watermelon
Leafy Greens*	Yellow summer
	squash

such as spinach and kale

Nonperishable Foods

Nonperishable foods, such as canned goods, pasta, flour, cereal, peanut butter, and rice, should be stored in a dark, dry, cool space kept at room temperature (59°F–86°F). These "shelf-stable" foods do best in a cupboard or pantry away from the range, oven, dishwasher, or refrigerator exhaust.

While warm and humid climates can shorten the shelf life of most foods, even canned goods can become damaged in temperatures exceeding 100°F. Because some nonperishable foods are not store-dated, remember to write the purchase date on the container, as there is a LIMIT to the length of time all foods, even cans, will remain good. Date labeling will also allow you to determine which products are oldest and should be consumed first. See the "Food Storage and Longevity Charts" in this book for more information and specific details.

Canned Foods Discard foods from cans that are leaking, bulging, dented, or rusty. While most canned foods enjoy a long shelf life when properly stored and remain safe to eat for years, in time the color, flavor, texture, and nutritional value of canned food will deteriorate.

So keep in mind, both when shopping and before using, that dusty cans or torn labels may indicate old stock. Depending on the contents, the shelf life of canned food varies. In general, use the following as a guide, but for specific information refer to the "Food Storage and Longevity Charts" in this book.

- **Low-acid canned foods**: Canned foods such as meat, poultry, seafood, stews, soup (except tomato), pasta products, potatoes, corn, carrots, spinach, beans, beets, peas, and pumpkin maintain their quality for two to five years.
- **High-acid canned foods**: Canned foods such as tomato products, fruits, sauerkraut, and vinegar-based sauces and salad dressings maintain their quality for 12 to 18 months.

- **Canned fruit juices**: Maintain their quality for approximately nine months.
- **Canned ham**: Always check the label for proper storage suggestions. Not all canned ham is shelf-stable.

Flour Since flour absorbs odor, it should be stored in an airtight container away from soap powders, medicines, onions, or anything with a strong odor. In hot and humid climates, purchase flour in small quantities and store in the refrigerator.

Refrigerator Safety

Proper Temperature The proper temperature setting for a refrigerator is 40°F or below. Temperatures can be checked with a thermometer specially made for the refrigerator and freezer and should be checked often. Thermometers can be purchased at most grocery stores for less than $5. To maintain the proper temperature, air must be able to circulate around the food. When the refrigerator is overloaded, air becomes trapped and appropriate temperatures are difficult to maintain. Also helpful in maintaining the proper temperature is deciding which items should come out before opening the refrigerator door. As cool air quickly rushes out, warm air rushes in and compromises the ideal temperature.

To keep freezer items as fresh as possible (and keep microorganisms from multiplying), freezer temperatures should remain at 0°F or below and be checked regularly with a store-bought thermometer. Placing warm leftovers in small containers or cooling food in an ice bath before freezing will help maintain the proper freezer temperature. The flavor, texture, and quality of food kept in the freezer may deteriorate over time, especially fatty and oily foods like salmon and bacon. Therefore, most food stored longer than 12 months should be discarded. For specific information, refer to the "Food Storage and Longevity Charts" in this book.

Check for the following should an incorrect refrigerator or freezer temperature occur:

- **Altered temperature setting** Reset the temperature control device in the unit, and monitor the temperature with a refrigerator/freezer thermometer until the appropriate temperature returns (40°F or below in the refrigerator and 0°F or below in the freezer).
- **Warm and hot food** Either separate large amounts of hot foods into multiple small containers so they will cool quickly, or place large containers of hot food in an ice bath before placing in the refrigerator or freezer. Warm and hot foods placed in the refrigerator or freezer can quickly raise the temperature.
- **Power/malfunctioning problems** Ensure that the unit is plugged in and the circuit breaker has not been tripped before calling for service.

Preservation Without Power On average, food will remain chilled for about four hours in a refrigerator without power, as long as the door is kept shut. If you think the power will be out for several days, transfer perishable foods from the refrigerator to the freezer. Then load the freezer with blocks of ice, bags of ice, or dry ice. If a refrigerator is malfunctioning or if the power goes out, place ice inside the unit and keep the door closed, or transfer food to another unit. Use a refrigerator thermometer to check the temperature. If the temperature rises above 40°F for two hours or more, throw out all perishables and any food that has an unusual odor, color, or texture.

Food can remain frozen in a full freezer for about two days, and about one day in a freezer that is half full, if the door remains closed. If power is lost, place dry ice or block ice inside the unit and keep the door closed, or transfer food to an insulated cooler and keep it continually iced. If, when the power was out, the temperature was above 0°F but below 40°F for more than two hours, each package should be evaluated. If ice crystals are present, the food can be refrozen—with the exception of ice cream and frozen yogurt, which should be discarded. If items have thawed, cook them immediately or transfer them to the refrigerator. However, if the temperature was above 40°F for two hours or more, all items should be thrown out.

Moisture When the refrigerator is running properly, air is constantly circulating. This helps to prevent the high moisture levels that support bacteria growth. (However, keep in mind that foods not wrapped and sealed properly can dry out from this air motion.)

Many refrigerators are now equipped with Anti-Sweat/ Energy Saver units that help reduce the amount of internal humidity. Keeping the switch in the "OFF" position in the winter, when the outside air is less humid, and in the "ON" position during the summer, when the outside air is more humid, will help maintain the appropriate humidity level.

Here are additional ways to help regulate humidity levels:

• Arrange the shelves and food items so air can circulate properly.

- Seal liquids and high-moisture foods.
- Keep the refrigerator and freezer half full.
- Keep the doors closed as much as possible.
- Clean the condenser coils (located on the back of the refrigerator) twice a year.
- Make sure that the door seals are in good condition and clean.

Freezing When It's Fresh

While the quality of nonfrozen foods diminishes rapidly over time, food wrapped properly and stored in the freezer at 0°F or below will retain good flavor and texture, as well as retain all or nearly all the nutrients it had when it was fresh. Therefore, it's best to freeze food when it's at its peak in terms of freshness. And again, date labeling all frozen food will help ensure food is consumed in the appropriate amount of time.

Packaging Food for the Freezer

Proper packaging helps maintain the food's quality and prevents freezer burn. Freezer burn is caused by dehydration of food due to improper wrapping. Leaving food in its original packaging and then overwrapping with proper freezing material will help maintain the food's quality by protecting it from bacteria and frost. Eliminating all air from the package will also help prevent freezer burn. While freezer burn diminishes quality and taste, food with freezer burn is safe to eat. Freezer burn can be cut off the food either before or after cooking.

Freezer Packaging Materials:

Freezer packaging materials should be resistant to moisture, vapor, oil, grease, and water. They should be durable and leak-proof and able to protect food from absorption of off-flavors and odors. Materials also should be easy to seal and mark, and resistant to becoming brittle or cracking at low temperatures.

Examples of Good Freezing Materials:

- Rigid containers made of aluminum, plastic, or tin
- Glass jars made for canning and freezing
- Heavily waxed cardboard
- Plastic wraps that are moisture- and vapor-resistant
- Zip-top plastic bags rated for freezer use
- Laminated paper made for freezer use
- Heavy-duty aluminum foil wrapped in zip-top plastic bags

Materials That Should Not Be Used for Freezing:

- Wax paper
- Bread wrappers
- Glass jars not made for freezing
- Cardboard cartons (e.g., milk cartons)

Food Storage and Longevity Charts

By knowing how, where, and how long to store your food, you can be sure of four things:

1. Your food will be as safe to eat as possible.
2. Desirable flavor and texture will be retained.
3. A high level of nutrients will be maintained.
4. You won't waste money on spoiled food.

NOTE: If a product has a "Use By" date, follow that date. If a product has a "Sell By" date or if it has no date, use it within the times shown in the following charts.

Much of the information in the "Food Storage and Longevity Charts" comes from the Food Keeper consumer brochure with permission from the Food Marketing Institute. This brochure was developed by the Food Marketing Institute with the Cornell University Institute of Food Science, the USDA's Meat and Poultry Hotline, and the FDA's Center for Food Safety and Applied Nutrition.

Bakery Items	Shelf	Refrigerator	Freezer*
Bread, commercial	2-4 days	7-14 days	3 months
Bread, flat	2-4 days	4-7 days	4 months
Cake, angel food**	1-2 days	7 days	2 months

Optimum freezing times for best quality.

**Any breads that contain perishable ingredients such as meat, hard-cooked eggs, or custard should be refrigerated within two hours.*

***Refrigerate any cake with frosting made of cream cheese, buttercream, whipped cream, or eggs.*

Bakery Items	Shelf	Refrigerator	Freezer*
Cake, chiffon	1-2 days	7 days	2 months
Cake, chocolate***	1-2 days	7 days	4 months
Cake, pound	3-4 days	7 days	6 months
Cake, sponge	1-2 days	1 week	2 months
Cheesecake	—	7 days	2-3 months
Cookies, bakery or homemade	2-3 weeks	2 months	8-12 months
Croissants, butter	1 day	7 days	2 months
Doughnuts, cake	1-2 days	7 days	1 month
Doughnuts, dairy-cream-filled	—	3-4 days	—
Doughnuts, glazed	1-2 days	7 days	1 month
Fruitcake	1 month	6 months	1 year
Muffins	1-2 days	7 days	2 months
Pastries, Danish	1-2 days	7 days	2 months
Pie, cream	—	3-4 days	—
Pie, cream, frozen	—	—	6 months
Pie, fruit	1-2 days	7 days	8 months
Pie, mincemeat	2 hours	7 days	8 months
Pie, pecan	2 hours	3-4 days	1-2 months
Pie, pumpkin	2 hours	3-4 days	1-2 months
Pitas	2-4 days	4-7 days	4 months
Quiche	2 hours	3-4 days	2 months
Rolls, baked	3-4 days	7 days	2 months
Rolls, meat- or vegetable-filled	2 hours	3-4 days	2 months
Rolls, yeast	3-4 days	7 days	2 months
Tortillas	2-4 days	4-7 days	4 months

* Optimum freezing times for best quality.

Foods Purchased Frozen

Note: Properly packaged frozen foods will hold their flavor and nutrients for the times listed below. After these times, the flavor and nutrient value may diminish; however, the food is still safe to eat.

Frozen Foods	Freezer*	Refrigerator, after thawing
Bagels	2 months	1-2 weeks
Bread dough, commercial	Use-by date	After baking, 4-7 days
Burritos	2 months	3-4 days
Egg substitutes	1 year	Date on carton
Fish, breaded	3-6 months	Do not defrost; cook frozen
Fish, raw	6 months	1-2 days
Fruit such as berries, melons	4-6 months	4-5 days
Guacamole	3-4 months	3-4 days
Ice cream	2-4 months	—
Juice concentrates	6-12 months	7-10 days
Lobster tails	3 months	2 days
Pancakes	2 months	3-4 days
Pie crust	1 year	—
Popsicles	Indefinitely	—
Potatoes	1 year	—
Sausages, precooked	1-2 months	7 days
Sausages, uncooked	1-2 months	1-2 days
Shellfish	1 year	1-2 days

Optimum freezing times for best quality.

Frozen Foods	Freezer*	Refrigerator, after thawing
Sherbet	2-4 months	—
Shrimp	1 year	1-2 days
Sorbet	2-4 months	—
Topping, whipped	6 months	2 weeks
TV dinners, entrees, breakfast	3 months	Do not defrost; cook frozen
Vegetables	8 months	3-4 days
Waffles	2 months	3-4 days

Foods Purchased Refrigerated

Note: The information listed in this section outlines how long products last beyond their "Best When Used By" or "Sell By" date. For example, if you purchase milk that has a "Sell By" date of November 1, the milk will retain its freshness for as many as five days, or up to November 6. All dates are based on the assumption that the food has been properly stored.

Dairy products	Refrigerator	Freezer*
Butter	1-3 months	6-9 months
Buttermilk	7-14 days	3 months
Cheese, cottage	1 week	Doesn't freeze well
Cheese, cream	2 weeks	Doesn't freeze well
Cheese, hard (such as Cheddar, Swiss)	6 months unopened; 3-4 weeks opened	6 months

* Optimum freezing times for best quality.

Dairy products	Refrigerator	Freezer*
Cheese, Parmesan – grated	1 month, opened	3-4 months
Cheese, processed slices	1-2 months	Doesn't freeze well
Cheese, ricotta	1 week	Doesn't freeze well
Cheese, shredded	1 month	3-4 months
Cheese, soft (such as Brie, Bel Paese)	1 week	6 months
Cream, half and half	3-4 days	4 months
Kefir (fermented milk)	1 week after date on carton; 1-2 days opened	Do not freeze
Milk	Up to 7 days after date printed on carton	3 months
Pudding	Package date; 2 days after opening	Do not freeze
Sour cream	1-3 weeks	Doesn't freeze well
Whipped cream, aerosol can	3-4 weeks	Do not freeze
Whipped topping, aerosol can, nondairy	3 months	Do not freeze
Whipping cream, sweetened	1 day	1-2 months
Whipping cream, ultra-pasteurized	1 month	Do not freeze
Yogurt	7-14 days after the "sell by" date	1-2 months

Optimum freezing times for best quality.

Deli foods	Refrigerator	Freezer*
Entrees, cold or hot	3-4 days	2-3 months
Meat, store-sliced deli	3-5 days	1-2 months
Salads	3-5 days	Do not freeze

Dough	Refrigerator	Freezer*
Biscuits, tube-canned	Use-by date	Do not freeze
Cookie dough	Use-by date, open or unopened	2 months
Pasta, fresh	1-2 days or use-by date on package	2 months
Pie crust, ready-to-bake	Use-by date	2 months
Pizza dough, tube-canned	Use-by date	Do not freeze
Rolls, tube-canned	Use-by date	Do not freeze

Egg Products	Refrigerator	Freezer*
Egg substitutes, opened	3 days	Do not freeze
Egg substitutes, unopened	10 days	Do not freeze
Eggnog, commercial	3-5 days	6 months

* Optimum freezing times for best quality.

Egg Products	Refrigerator	Freezer*
Eggs, hard-cooked	7 days	Do not freeze well
Eggs, in shell	3-5 weeks	Do not freeze
Eggs, raw whites	2-4 days	1 year
Eggs, raw yolks	2-4 days	1 year

Fish	Refrigerator	Freezer*
Caviar, nonpasteurized, fresh	6 months unopened, 2 days after opening	Do not freeze
Caviar, pasteurized, vacuum-packaged	1 year unopened; 2 days after opening	Do not freeze
Fish, cooked	3-4 days	1-2 months
Fish, fatty (bluefish, mackerel, salmon, etc.)	1-2 days	2-3 months
Fish, lean (cod, flounder, haddock, sole, etc.)	1-2 days	6-8 months
Fish, smoked	14 days (or date on vacuum package)	2 months in vacuum pkg.
Surimi	3-4 days (or date on package)	9 months

Meat, Fresh	Refrigerator	Freezer*
Beef, fresh	3-5 days	4-12 months

* Optimum freezing times for best quality.

Meat, Fresh	Refrigerator	Freezer*
Cooked meats (after home cooking)	3-4 days	2-3 months
Ground meat	1-2 days	3-4 months
Lamb, fresh	3-5 days	4-12 months
Pork, fresh	3-5 days	4-12 months
Roasts, fresh	3-5 days	4-12 months
Steaks, fresh	3-5 days	4-12 months
Variety meats (liver, tongue, chitterlings, etc.)	1-2 days	3-4 months
Veal chops, fresh	3-5 days	4-12 months

Meat, Smoked or Processed	Refrigerator	Freezer*
Bacon	1 week	1 month
Corned beef, in pouch with pickling juices	5-7 days	1 month
Ham, canned ("keep refrigerated" label)	6-9 months	Do not freeze
Ham, fully cooked, slices, or halves	3-4 days	1-2 months
Ham, fully cooked, whole	1 week	1-2 months
Hot dogs, after opening	1 week	1-2 months

* Optimum freezing times for best quality.

Meat, Smoked or Processed	Refrigerator	Freezer*
Hot dogs, sealed in package	2 weeks	1-2 months
Lunch meats, after opening	3-5 days	1-2 months
Lunch meats, sealed in package	2 weeks	1-2 months
Sausage, hard, dry (pepperoni), sliced	2-3 weeks	1-2 months
Sausage, raw, bulk type	1-2 days	1-2 months
Sausage, smoked links, patties	1 week	1-2 months

Miscellaneous	Refrigerator	Freezer*
Beverages, fruit	3 weeks, unopened	—
Dip, sour-cream-based	2 weeks	Doesn't freeze well
Juice in cartons, fruit drinks, punch	7-10 days opened, 3 weeks unopened	8-12 months
Margarine	4-5 months	1 year
Miso	3 months	Do not freeze
Pesto, refrigerated	Date on carton; 3 days after opening	1-2 months
Rice beverage	7-10 days	Do not freeze

* Optimum freezing times for best quality.

Miscellaneous	Refrigerator	Freezer*
Salsa, refrigerated	Date on carton; 3 days after opening	1-2 months
Soy beverage	7-10 days	Do not freeze
Tofu	1 week or date on package	5 months

Poultry, Fresh	Refrigerator	Freezer*
Chicken or turkey, parts	1-2 days	9 months
Duckling or goose, whole	1-2 days	6 months
Giblets	1-2 days	3-4 months
Turkey, ground	1-2 days	3-4 months

Poultry, Cooked or Processed	Refrigerator	Freezer*
Chicken, fried	3-4 days	4 months
Chicken or turkey, ground	1-2 days	3-4 months
Chicken, nuggets, patties	1-2 days	1-3 months
Chicken, rotisserie	3-4 days	4 months
Cooked poultry dishes	3-4 days	4-6 months
Lunch meats, after opening	3-5 days	1-2 months

Optimum freezing times for best quality.

Poultry, Cooked or Processed	Refrigerator	Freezer*
Lunch meats, sealed in package	2 weeks	1-2 months
Pieces covered with broth or gravy	1-2 days	6 months

Shellfish	Refrigerator	Freezer*
Clams, live	1-2 days	2-3 months
Clams, shucked	1-2 days	3-4 months
Crabmeat, fresh	1-2 days	4 months
Crabmeat, pasteurized	6 months unopened, 3-5 days opened	4 months
Crab, live	1-2 days	2-3 months
Crayfish	1-2 days	3-6 months
Lobster, live	1-2 days	2-3 months
Mussels, live	1-2 days	2-3 months
Mussels, shucked	1-2 days	3-4 months
Oysters, live	1-2 days	2-3 months
Oysters, shucked	1-2 days	3-4 months
Scallops	1-2 days	3-6 months
Shellfish, cooked	3-4 days	3 months
Shrimp	1-2 days	3-6 months
Squid	1-2 days	3-6 months

* Optimum freezing times for best quality.

Fresh Foods

Fruits	Shelf	Refrigerator	Freezer*
Acai berries	—	—	Pureed, 5 years
Apples	1-2 days	3 weeks	Cooked, 8 months
Apricots	Until ripe	2-3 days	—
Avocados	Until ripe	3-4 days	—
Bananas	Until ripe	2 days, skin will blacken	Whole peeled, 1 month
Berries	—	1-2 days	4 months
Cantaloupes	1-2 days, uncut until ripe	3-4 days, cut	Balls, 1 month
Carambola	2-3 days	2 weeks	—
Cherimoya	Until ripe	—	Pureed or juiced, several weeks
Cherries	—	1-2 days	4 months
Citrus fruit	Up to 10 days	1-2 weeks	—
Coconuts	1 week	2-3 weeks, or 4 days if grated	Shredded, 6 months
Dates	4 weeks	6-12 months	1 year
Dragon fruit	—	3 months (uncut in paper bag)	3 months (as pulp)
Durian	2-3 days	Several days	3 months

* Optimum freezing times for best quality.

Fruits	Shelf	Refrigerator	Freezer*
Figs, fresh	—	2-3 days	10-12 months
Grapefruit	7-10 days	1-2 weeks	—
Grapes	1 day	1 week	Whole, 1 month
Guava	2-5 days, until ripe	3-4 days	10-12 months
Honeydew melon	1-2 days, uncut until ripe	3-4 days, cut	Balls, 1 month
Kiwifruits	Until ripe	3-4 days	—
Kumquats	3-4 days	3 weeks	Pureed, 6 months
Lemons	7-10 days	1-2 weeks	—
Limes	7-10 days	1-2 weeks	—
Lychees	2-3 days	5 weeks	Several weeks
Mangos	3-5 days	1 week	—
Mangosteen	—	2 weeks	—
Nectarines	Until ripe	3-4 days	Sliced with lemon juice & sugar, 2 months
Oranges	10 days	1-2 weeks	—
Papayas	3-5 days	1 week	—
Passionfruit	1-2 days	1 week	6-8 months
Peaches	Until ripe	3-4 days	Sliced with lemon juice & sugar, 2 months
Pears	3-5 days	3-4 days	—
Pineapples	1-2 days	1-7 days	—

* Optimum freezing times for best quality.

Fruits	Shelf	Refrigerator	Freezer*
Plums	3-5 days	3-4 days	—
Pomegranates	5-8 days	2-3 weeks	—
Quinces	2-5 days	2-3 weeks	2 months
Sapodilla	7-10 days	2-3 weeks	1 month
Strawberries	—	1-2 days	4 months
Tangerines	2-3 weeks	2 weeks	—
Watermelons	1-2 days, uncut until ripe	3-4 days, cut	Balls, 1 month

Vegetables	Shelf	Refrigerator	Blanched, Cooked, or Frozen
Artichokes, whole	1-2 days	1-2 weeks	—
Asparagus	—	3-4 days	8 months
Beans, green/snap/wax	—	3-4 days	8 months
Beets	1 day	7-10 days	6-8 months
Bok choy	—	2-3 days	10-12 months
Broccoli	—	3-5 days	10-12 months
Brussels sprouts	—	3-5 days	10-12 months
Cabbage, green/red	—	1-2 weeks	10-12 months
Carrots	—	2-4 weeks	10-12 months
Cauliflower	—	2 weeks	10-12 months
Celery	—	1-2 weeks	10-12 months
Cilantro	1-3 days	1 week	1-2 months
Corn on the cob	—	1-2 days	8 months
Cucumbers	—	4-5 days	—

* Optimum freezing times for best quality.

Vegetables	Shelf	Refrigerator	Blanched, Cooked, or Frozen
Eggplants	1 day	3-4 days	6-8 months
Garlic	1 month	1-2 weeks	1 month
Ginger root	1-2 days	1-3 weeks	1-2 months
Greens, leafy	—	1-2 days	10-12 months
Herbs, fresh	—	7-10 days	1-2 months
Leeks	—	1-2 weeks	10-12 months
Lettuce, iceberg	—	1-2 weeks	—
Lettuce, leaf	—	3-7 days	—
Lettuce, precut/washed	—	Until date on package	—
Lettuce, romaine	—	3-7 days	—
Mushrooms	—	2-3 days	10-12 months
Okra	—	2-3 days	10-12 months
Onions, dry	2-3 weeks	2 months	10-12 months
Onions, green (scallions)	—	1-2 weeks	10-12 months
Parsley	—	1 week	1-2 months
Parsnips	—	2 weeks	10-12 months
Peppers, bell	—	4-5 days	6-8 months
Peppers, chili		4-5 days	6-8 months
Potatoes, white	1-2 months	1-2 weeks	Cooked and mashed, 10-12 months
Potatoes, sweet	2 weeks	2-3 months	—
Radishes	—	2 weeks	—
Rutabagas	1 week	2 weeks	8-10 months
Spinach, leaf	—	1-2 days	Cooked, 10-12 months
Squash, summer	—	4-5 days	10-12 months

Vegetables	Shelf	Refrigerator	Blanched, Cooked, or Frozen
Squash, winter	1 week	2 weeks	10-12 months
Tomatoes	Until ripe	2-3 days	2 months
Turnips	—	2 weeks	8-10 months

Shelf Foods

Shelf Foods	Unopened on Shelf	Opened on Shelf	Opened, Refrigerator
Beans, dried	1 year	1 year	—
Bouillon cubes, granules	2 years	—	—
Candy, chocolate	1 year	—	—
Candy, hard	Indefinitely (Keep away from moisture)	—	—
Canned goods, low-acid (such as meat, poultry, fish, gravy, stew, soups, beans, carrots, corn, pasta, peas, potatoes, spinach)	2-5 years	—	3-4 days

Shelf Foods	Unopened on Shelf	Opened on Shelf	Opened, Refrigerator
Canned goods, high-acid (such as juices, fruit, pickles, sauerkraut, tomato soup, and foods in vinegar-based sauce)	12-18 months	—	5-7 days
Cereal, cook before eating (oatmeal, etc.)	1 year	6-12 months	—
Cereal, ready-to-eat	6-12 months	3 months	—
Cheese, aerosol can	Extended shelf life	—	—
Cookies, packaged	2 months	4 weeks	8-12 months frozen
Crackers	8 months	1 month	Frozen or refrigerated 3-4 months
Diet powder mixes	6 months	3 months	—
Fruits, dried	6 months	—	6 months
Fruit Roll-Ups®	1 year	—	—
Gelatin, flavored	18 months	Use all or reseal for 3-4 months	—
Gelatin, unflavored	3 years	Use all or reseal for 3-4 months	—
Jerky, commercially dried	1 year	—	2-3 months
Jerky, homemade	—	1-2 months	1-2 months
Lentils, dried	1 year	1 year	—
Marshmallows	2-4 months	1 month	—
Marshmallow crème	2-4 months	1 month	—

Shelf Foods	Unopened on Shelf	Opened on Shelf	Opened, Refrigerator
Mushrooms, dried	6 months	3 months	—
Nuts, jars or cans	1 year	1 month	4-6 months; frozen 9-12 months
Pasta, dry, made without eggs	2 years	1 year	—
Pasta, dry, egg noodles	2 years	1-2 months	—
Peanut butter, commercial	6-9 months	2-3 months	—
Peas, dried split	1 year	1 year	—
Pectin	Use-by date	1 month	—
Popcorn, dry kernels in jar	2 years	1 year	—
Popcorn, commercially popped in bags	2-3 months	1-2 weeks	—
Popcorn, microwave packets	1 year	1-2 days popped	—
Potato chips	2 months	1-2 weeks	—
Potatoes, instant	6-12 months	6-12 months	—
Pudding mixes	1 year	3-4 months	—
Rice, brown	1 year	1 year	6 months
Rice, flavored	6 months	Use entire amt.	6 months
Rice, herb mixes	6 months	Use entire amt.	6 months
Rice, white	2 years	1 year	6 months
Rice, wild	2 years	1 year	6 months
Sauce mixes, nondairy, spaghetti, taco, etc.	2 years	Use entire amt.	—
Soup mixes	1 year	Use entire amt.	—
Tapioca	1 year	1 year	—

Shelf Foods	Unopened on Shelf	Opened on Shelf	Opened, Refrigerator
Toaster pastries, fruit-filled	6 months	Keep foil packets sealed	—
Toaster pastries, non-fruit fillings	9 months	Keep foil packets sealed	—
Tomatoes, sun-dried, packed in cellophane	9 months	3-6 months	6-12 months
Tomatoes, sun-dried, packed in oil	1 year	3-6 months	6-12 months

Shelf-Stable Foods

Baby Food, Jars or Cans	Unopened on Shelf	Opened on Shelf	Opened, Refrigerator
Cereal, dry mixed	Use-by date	2 months	—
Formula	Use-by date	—	1-2 days
Fruits and vegetables	Use-by date	—	2-3 days
Meat and eggs	Use-by date	—	1 day

Baking Ingredients	Unopened on Shelf	Opened on Shelf	Opened, Refrigerator
Baking cocoa	Indefinitely	1 year	—
Baking powder	6 months	3 months	—
Baking soda	18 months	6 months	—

Baking Ingredients	Unopened on Shelf	Opened on Shelf	Opened, Refrigerator
Biscuit or pancake mix	15 months	Pkg. use-by date	—
Bread mix	12-18 months	Pkg. use-by date	—
Brownie mix	12-18 months	Pkg. use-by date	—
Cake mix	12-18 months	Pkg. use-by date	—
Chocolate, unsweetened and semi-sweet, solid	18-24 months	1 year	—
Cornmeal, regular	6-12 months	—	1 year
Cornmeal, degerminated	6-12 months	—	1 year
Cornstarch	18 months	18 months	—
Corn syrup	3 years	3 years	—
Flour, white	6-12 months	6-8 months	—
Flour, whole wheat	1 month	—	6-8 months
Frosting, canned	3-10 months	—	1 week
Frosting mixes	8-12 months	3 months	—
Oil sprays, vegetable	2 years	1 year	—
Oils, nut	6 months	—	—
Oils, olive	6 months	1-3 months	4 months
Oils, vegetable	6 months	1-3 months	4 months
Soy flour, full-fat	2 months	—	6 months
Soy flour, low-fat	1 year	1 year	—
Shortening, solid	8 months	3 months	—
Sugar, brown	4 months	Indefinitely	—
Sugar, confectioners	18 months	Indefinitely	—
Sugar, granulated	2 years	Indefinitely	—
Sugar substitutes	2 years	Indefinitely	—

Beverages and Drink Mixes	Unopened on Shelf	Opened on Shelf	Opened, Refrigerator
Cocoa and cocoa mixes	Indefinitely	1 year	—
Coffee, ground, in cans	2 years	—	2 weeks
Coffee, instant, jars, and tins	1 year	2-3 months	2 weeks
Coffee, whole beans, non-vacuum bag	1-3 weeks	1 week	2 weeks
Juice, boxes	4-6 months	—	8-12 days
Lemon juice, bottled	15 months unopened	—	4-6 months
Lemon juice, fresh	—	—	1 week
Milk, canned, evaporated	1 year	—	4-5 days
Sodas, diet, bottled	3 months after date	—	2-3 days
Sodas, diet, canned	3 months after date	—	2-3 days
Sodas, regular, bottled	3 months after date	—	2-3 days
Sodas, regular, canned	9 months after date	—	—
Tea, bags	18 months	1 year	—
Tea, instant	3 years	6-12 months	—
Tea, loose	2 years	6-12 months	—
Water, bottled	1-2 years	3 months	—

Condiments	Unopened on Shelf	Opened on Shelf	Opened, Refrigerator
Barbecue sauce, bottled	1 year	1 month	4 months

Condiments	Unopened on Shelf	Opened on Shelf	Opened, Refrigerator
Chili sauce	1 year	1 month	6 months
Chocolate syrup	2 years	—	6 months
Chutney	1 year	—	1-2 months
Cocktail sauce	1 year	1 month	6 months
Cream sauces with milk solids	1 year	—	—
Gravy, jars and cans	2-5 years	—	1-2 days
Gravy mix, dry	2 years	Mix entire packet	1-2 days
Honey	1 year	1 year	—
Horseradish, in jar	1 year	—	3-4 months
Jams	1 year	—	6 months
Jellies	1 year	—	6 months
Ketchup, tomato	1 year	1 month	6 months
Mayonnaise, commercial	2-3 months	—	2 months
Molasses	1 year	6 months	—
Mustard	1 year	1-2 months	1 year
Olives, black and green	12-18 months	—	2 weeks
Pickles	1 year	—	1-2 months
Preserves	1 year	—	6 months
Relish, pickle (glass container)	2 years	—	1-2 months
Relish, pickle (plastic container)	15 months	—	1-2 months
Salad dressings, commercial, bottled	10-12 months	—	1-3 months
Salsa, picante	1 year	—	2-4 weeks
Salsa, taco	1 year	—	1 month
Soy sauce	3 years	6-9 months	—

Condiments	Unopened on Shelf	Opened on Shelf	Opened, Refrigerator
Sweet-and-sour sauce	3 years	—	6-9 months
Syrup, pancake, maple & other flavors	1 year	1 year	—
Syrup, maple, pure genuine	1 year	—	1 year
Worcestershire sauce	1 year	1 year	—

Spices, Additives, Etc	Unopened on Shelf	Opened on Shelf	Opened, Refrigerator
Bacon bits, imitation	4 months	4 months	—
Chili powder	2 years	—	Store in refrigerator
Extracts, vanilla, lemon, etc.	3 years	1 year	—
Garlic, chopped, commercial jars	18 months	—	Use by date on jar
Herbs, dried	1-2 years	Store in cool dark place 1 year	—
Paprika powder	2 years	Included in total	—
Red pepper powder	2 years	Included in total	Store in refrigerator
Spices, ground	2-3 years	Included in total	—
Spices, whole	2-4 years	Included in total	—
Vinegar	2 years	1 year	—

Spices, Additives, Etc	Unopened on Shelf	Opened on Shelf	Opened, Refrigerator
Yeast, dry, packets and jars	Use-by date	—	Refrigerate open jars

PART V
IN THE KITCHEN

Creating a Clean and Sanitized Environment

No matter how carefully food items are selected and stored, food safety is easily jeopardized by preparation areas that have not been adequately cleaned. Proper washing and sanitizing of hands, preparation surfaces, cutting boards, cooking utensils, and sinks are essential. A clean kitchen environment is where safe and healthy meals begin.

Clean and Sanitized Hands

Safe food preparation begins with clean and sanitized hands. According to the CDC, the best way to clean your hands is by washing them with soap and water for at least 20 seconds. Be sure to lather and wash all sides of your hands, between your fingers, and under your nails. Rinse your hands thoroughly using clean running water, and dry them with a clean hand towel or a paper towel, or air dry them.

If soap and water are not available, alcohol-based hand sanitizers (with at least 60 percent alcohol) can be used to reduce the amount of germs on your hands. Read the label on the hand sanitizer container to know the proper amount to use. Apply the sanitizer to one palm and then rub your hands together so all surfaces of your hands and fingers are covered. Allow your hands to air dry.

Hands should be washed before, during, and after preparing food; after using the toilet, after changing diapers or cleaning a child who has used the toilet; and after blowing your nose, coughing, or sneezing. You should also clean your hands after touching an animal, animal feed, animal waste, pet food, or pet treats. Finally, be sure to wash your hands after touching the garbage can. It's also important to cover cuts and sores with plastic or rubber gloves.

Countertops and Sinks

Cleaning and sanitizing the food preparation area of visible food soil and dirt will eliminate the source of bacteria and other germs. Furthermore, sanitizing/disinfecting the area on a regular basis with commercial cleaners, wipes, or bleach solutions (allowing to sit for two minutes) will reduce germs to a safe level by eliminating over 99 percent of harmful bacteria.

An economical and effective alternative to commercial cleaners and wipes is a homemade liquid bleach solution (see ingredients below), which is preferred by the Food & Drug Administration for disinfecting food preparation areas. Liquid bleach can be made in large amounts, then stored in a labeled spray bottle with other household cleaners.

Always read and follow precautions and usage instructions before using cleaning products. Always store cleaning products out of reach of children.

To help reduce the amount of bacteria in your kitchen sink and drain, always pour unused sanitizing and disinfecting solutions in the sink. Food particles in the drain and disposal combined with high levels of moisture create an environment that is ideal for bacterial growth. To deodorize, flush the drain first, then pour one cup of bleach into the drain, followed by flushing with hot water.

Paper towels are preferred for cleaning and drying cooking surfaces and utensils, as soiled cloth towels may spread bacteria.

Homemade Sanitizing/Disinfecting Solutions

Harmful germs and bacteria can easily spread through the entire kitchen, resulting in cross-contamination to countertops, utensils, and cutting boards. Raw meat, poultry, fish, and their juices should be kept away from other foods, especially ready-to-eat products. By avoiding cross-contamination, you can reduce the risk of foodborne illness to yourself and your family.

Homemade sanitizing solutions are an inexpensive and effective means of ensuring that your kitchen environment is clean and free of bacteria and germs.

For nonporous surfaces (plastic, stainless, glassware, granite, marble, countertops):

- Wash or rinse with liquid dishwashing detergent and water.
- Create a bleach solution using two teaspoons of liquid bleach per gallon of water.
- Cover surface with/soak surface in bleach solution, let stand for two minutes, and allow to air dry.

For porous surfaces (wood, rubber, or soft plastics):

- Create a bleach solution using two tablespoons of liquid bleach per gallon of water.
- Wash the surface with dishwashing detergent and

rinse with water.

- Cover surface with/soak surface in bleach solution. Let stand for two minutes and air dry.
- Rinse with water; do not soak overnight.

NOTE: *Do not use bleach solutions on steel, aluminum, silver, or chipped enamel.*

TIP: HYDROGEN PEROXIDE AND VINEGAR SOLUTION

Another effective homemade cleaning solution is a combination of hydrogen peroxide and vinegar (apple cider or white). Keep each in its own spray bottle and apply equal amounts to the surface to be cleaned. Let the solution sit for five minutes to completely sanitize, then wipe dry.

Cutting Board Safety

The safest cutting board practice is to have **two cutting boards** on hand: one for ready-to-eat foods like fruits, vegetables, and cooked foods; and a separate board for raw meats, poultry, and seafood. This will reduce the chance of unwanted cross-contamination.

No matter what type of food is prepared on a cutting board, the board should be cleaned and sanitized thoroughly after each use. For best results:

- Wash the cutting board surface with hot, soapy water, and then rinse it with plain water.
- Both porous (wood, stone) cutting boards and non-porous (acrylic, plastic, glass, and solid wood) boards can be sanitized with a solution of three tablespoons of unscented, liquid chlorine bleach per gallon of water. Cover the surface with the bleach solution and allow it to stand for several minutes. Rinse with water and air dry, or pat dry with clean paper towels.
- Nonporous acrylic, plastic, glass, and solid wood boards can be washed in a dishwasher.

TIP: REDUCING CUTTING BOARD ODORS

Reduce cutting board odors by rubbing the board with halved lemons and then rinsing with cold water.

Wood, Plastic, Stone, or Glass Cutting Board?

Most food safety specialists say that it is not the type of cutting board but whether or not it has a lot of scars. Bacteria can hide in the scars and crevices, resist cleaning and sanitizing, and multiply to dangerous levels. It's best to have a cutting board with a very hard surface that will resist scarring, be easy to clean and, therefore, be safe to use.

Towel and Sponge Safety

Dirty towels and sponges can be a persistent source of

germs in the kitchen. One should avoid wiping hands on a towel that has been used to clean a countertop or wipe up a spill. Kitchen towels should be washed in the washing machine, in hot water. Paper towels are always the safest choice for the kitchen.

A sponge can be cleaned and sanitized by regularly putting it in the silverware compartment of the dishwasher and washing it with the dishes. Another sanitizing method is to soak the sponge for five minutes in a sanitizing bleach solution (3/4 cup of liquid bleach to 1 gallon of water), rinse it in water, and then let it air dry.

TIP: LUNCHBOXES AND TOTES

Lunchboxes and tote bags should be washed after each use.

Thawing Food Safely

Improperly thawing food can cause foodborne illnesses. As food thaws, the outside becomes warm, creating an environment where bacteria can multiply, while the inside remains frozen. Never defrost food outdoors, in a cool room, or on the kitchen counter; these methods encourage the growth of harmful bacteria that may be present in the food. Below are four ways to safely thaw food:

In the Refrigerator Plan ahead! Thawing food in the refrigerator takes several hours. A five-pound frozen item may take as long as 24 hours to thaw in the refrigerator.

Thaw raw meats in leak-proof containers below all other foods; this will prevent juices from cross-contaminating other foods that may not be cooked. Food that has been thawed in the refrigerator is safe to refreeze without cooking, although some foods may lose their flavor when refrozen and then cooked.

In Water Fill the sink with cold water and place the food in the water inside a leak-proof container or plastic bag. Change the water every 30 minutes in an effort to keep bacteria from reaching high levels. No portion of the food should remain in the Danger Zone (between 40°–140°F) for more than two hours.

Thoroughly wash and disinfect the sink and your hands when you are finished.

In the Microwave Oven Microwave ovens, while quick and convenient, can be inconsistent in their heating, causing certain parts of the food to heat faster than others.

- Cover the microwave oven container with a lid or plastic wrap, leaving one corner turned back (do not let the plastic wrap touch the food as the food may absorb chemicals from the wrap).
- Rotate the food to help it thaw more evenly if the microwave oven doesn't include a carousel.
- Be sure to check for frozen spots. If frozen spots are found, stir, then continue microwaving until the food is completely thawed.
- Cook raw food immediately after thawing.

Caution! *Some stores now have metal scan tags that are part of meat packaging. These tags are used to help prevent theft; however, they will cause a fire if placed in the microwave oven, so be sure to remove all tags before cooking.*

From the Freezer to the Grill It is safe to cook frozen meat (such as premade hamburger patties) before it is thawed. However, since the center of the meat will take longer to cook, use a thermometer to ensure that the inside temperature of the food reaches a safe level (see temperature chart).

Washing Fruits and Vegetables

The cooking process (heat) kills most bacteria on fruits and vegetables. In addition to bacteria, most produce is wearing dirt, pesticide residues, and waxes that protect it along the journey from the fields to the dinner table and, therefore, should be carefully washed just prior to consumption. The most effective way to remove germs is to rinse and scrub fruits and vegetables under running water.

Because some pesticide residues are non-water-soluble (preventing rain wash-off in the field), water alone cannot remove all pesticide residues from produce.

Fit (www.tryfit.com) is an example of a grocery product found to safely remove wax, dirt, pesticides, and other residues from fruits and vegetables and then rinses away leaving no aftertaste or smell. All the ingredients in Fit are from 100 percent natural sources such as baking soda and citric acid.

Marinating Food

Food that is being marinated should be kept in the refrigerator to prevent bacterial growth. Marinating meats on the countertop allows dangerous bacteria to grow to high levels – levels too high for oven heat to kill.

Once the marinating process is complete, the marinade should be discarded. If you choose to brush on additional marinade during the cooking process, be sure to give the newly brushed marinade time to reach 140°F – killing any bacteria in the marinade left over from the meat. If you can't be sure it's reached 140°F, be safe and use fresh marinade. Be sure to use fresh marinade when applying to cooked meat.

Because marinade can be acidic, plastic or glass dishes should be used instead of metal.

Proportions As a rule, use ¼ cup of marinade per pound of meat. Most marinades use this proportion, and it is recommended that meats be marinated for 15 minutes to two hours prior to cooking.

PART VII
SAFE COOKING PRACTICES

Thermometers
  Types of Thermometers
  Thermometer Accuracy
  Proper Thermometer Placement
Cooking Eggs
  Keeping Eggs Safe
Homemade Flavored Oils and Vinegars
Cooking Meats and Poultry
  Minimal Internal Cooking Temperatures for Meat
Cooking Seafood
  *Minimal Internal Cooking Temperatures/Times for
    Shellfish*
  *Minimal Internal Cooking Temperatures/Times for
    Mollusks*
  *Minimal Internal Cooking Temperatures/Times for
    Fin Fish*
Preparing Wild Game
Cooking Stuffed Foods
Cooking in the Oven
Cooking in the Microwave Oven
Cleaning Up After Cooking
Managing Leftovers
Takeout Food
Bag Lunches

Thermometers

Certain foods require cooking to a specific internal temperature to be sure that potentially harmful bacteria are killed. If food is undercooked, there is a risk of acquiring a foodborne illness.

The best and simplest way to determine if food has been fully cooked (and not overcooked) is to **use a food thermometer.** A food thermometer can be used for all foods, not just meat. It measures the internal temperature of cooked meat, poultry, casseroles, and leftovers.

Types of Food Thermometers

Dial Oven-Safe   Oven-safe thermometers are made to remain in food while food is cooking. The thermometer should be placed in the thickest part of the meat. These thermometers are not appropriate for use with food that is thin, like chicken breast. The temperature indicator on oven-safe thermometers is designed to read within one to two minutes.

Instant-Read (Dial or Digital)   Instant-read thermometers are designed for a quick (15- to 20-second) read, when food is close to being thoroughly cooked. This type of thermometer is inserted into the thickest (center) part of the food (while outside of the oven), avoiding the bones in meat and poultry. It is then removed before placing food back into the oven.

Microwave-Oven Safe   Specifically designed for use in microwave ovens only.

Thermometer Accuracy

Some thermometers have test marks on them at 212°F (the boiling point of water at sea level), and most can be calibrated (adjusted) if necessary. To test a meat thermometer, insert at least two inches of the stem into boiling water and ensure that it reads 212°F.

Some thermometers have an adjustment nut under the dial that can be used to adjust the temperature readout if needed. Note: At high altitudes, water boils at a lower temperature. For example, at 5,000 feet above sea level, water boils at 202°F instead of 212°F.

Proper Thermometer Placement

The correct insertion point of the thermometer and the depth depends on the type and cut of meat. Follow these guidelines to obtain an accurate temperature reading:

- Meatloaf and boneless poultry: Place the thermometer in the thickest section of the meat.
- Ground beef patties: Insert the thermometer sideways.
- Poultry: Insert the thermometer in the inner thigh area near the breast; do not touch the bone.
- Beef, steaks, roasts, veal, ham, lamb, pork: Insert the thermometer into the thickest section, avoiding bones, fat, and gristle.

NOTE: *Thermometers should be cleaned before and after each use. Harmful germs and bacteria can be transferred from one food to another via a dirty thermometer.*

Cooking Eggs

Egg yolks may contain harmful bacteria that can cause foodborne illness; however, the likelihood of a single egg containing salmonella is low. Data from the CDC shows that the vast majority of salmonella (salmonellosis) caused by raw eggs happens in commercial kitchens and catering operations when a large number of raw eggs are used. This occurs when one egg containing salmonella contaminates all of the other safe eggs.

To reduce the risk of causing foodborne illness when cooking eggs at home, keep them refrigerated and cook them until the yolks are firm (they do not need to be rubbery, just not runny).

Minimum internal cooking temperatures for eggs:

- Eggs over easy or sunny-side up: Cook until the yolk and whites are firm.
- A recipe that contains eggs: Cook to 160°F.

Keeping Eggs Safe

If a recipe calls for raw eggs (e.g., Hollandaise sauce, eggnog, or Caesar salad), it is always best to choose a raw egg substitute or eggs that have been pasteurized in their shell (available in some parts of the U.S. – check the label on the carton). Egg substitutes are eggs that have been pasteurized (heated) to kill bacteria. This reduces the risk of foodborne illness. As with regular eggs, egg substitutes must be handled with care. Although pasteurization kills nearly all bacteria, some spoilage bacteria can still grow if the egg substitute is left out of the refrigerator.

The following is some basic information on egg safety:

- Raw eggs need to be refrigerated at 40°F or below.
- When cooking eggs, boil until the whites and yolks are firm.
- After an egg has been cooked, it should not remain in the Danger Zone (between 40°-140°F) for more than two hours (keep those Easter egg hunts short!).
- If cooked eggs are left out of the refrigerator for more than two hours, they should be discarded.

TIP: USING RAW EGGS

When raw eggs are used in cake and cookie recipes, the uncooked batter or dough should not be eaten.

Homemade Flavored Oils and Vinegars

Flavored oils and vinegars can be found in many restaurants and specialty shops. They seem like an easy item for the average consumer to make for personal consumption or as a gift. The reality is that making flavored oils can be especially hazardous. A person who does not know exactly how to proceed might create the perfect conditions for botulism toxin to be produced. For example, persons have become very ill and some deaths have occurred when raw garlic was placed in oil and left at room temperature, producing botulism toxin.

Food manufacturers know how to safely create flavored oils by adding certain preservatives or by cooking them to a very high temperature that inactivates bacteria. A good rule of thumb: If you cannot easily crumble an herb, it should not be placed in oil at room temperature. It is not recommended that you make these flavored oils at home. These types of products should only be made in commercial kitchens.

Flavored vinegars are much less hazardous because vinegar has a great deal of acid, and this prevents harmful bacteria from growing. However, precautions must still be taken. The best practice is to always refrigerate flavored vinegars. If there is a question about the acid content of the final homemade product, have it checked by a food laboratory.

Cooking Meats and Poultry

The USDA requires that meat and poultry be labeled with safe food handling instructions. This is because there is a chance that some meat and poultry might have bacteria that can cause a foodborne illness. Fortunately, it is very easy to kill these bacteria with proper cooking temperatures.

TIP: THAWING FROZEN POULTRY IN THE FRIDGE

Thaw a frozen bird (turkey, chicken, game hen, etc.) in the refrigerator to ensure even and safe cooking.

Minimum internal
cooking temperatures for meat:

Beef, veal, lamb, pork, steaks, and roasts

Medium-rare	145°F
Medium	160°F
Well-done	170°F

Ground products

Hamburgers	160°F
Beef, veal, lamb, and pork	160°F
Chicken and turkey	165°F

Poultry

Chicken	165°F
Turkey	165°F
Duck and Goose	165°F

Other meats

Ham	145°F
Sausage	160°F
Stuffed meats	165°F

Cooking Seafood

Properly cooking seafood, including shellfish (such as shrimp, crab, and lobster), mollusks (such as oysters, clams, mussels, and scallops), or fin fish (such as trout, catfish, and grouper), requires specific internal temperatures or, in some cases, cooking times, as follows:

Minimum internal cooking temperatures/times for shellfish:

Crab and whole lobster	145°F
Lobster tail	140°F
Shrimp	2-3 minutes per side (until opaque)

Minimum cooking time for mollusks:

Oysters, clams, and mussels	3-5 minutes (until shells open)
Scallops	2-3 minutes per side (until opaque and firm)

**Minimum internal cooking
temperatures for fin fish:**

Whole fillets	145°F (or until flesh is opaque and separates easily with a fork)
Groundfish	160°F
Scallops	2-3 minutes per side (until opaque)

While it is important for the elderly, children, and persons with chronic illnesses affecting their immune system to avoid eating uncooked or undercooked meat, poultry, or seafood, mollusks like oysters and clams pose special risks when they are eaten raw. Though state and federal government agencies monitor the waters from which shellfish can be legally harvested, there is always the chance they contain undetected levels of pollution and bacteria.

Preparing Wild Game

Because wild game such as deer, boar, and bear can sometimes carry parasites as a result of living in the wild, their meat should be cooked to 170°F to prevent foodborne illness.

Cooking Stuffed Foods

Stuffed foods such as pasta, chicken, and fish (e.g., manicotti, chicken cordon bleu, stuffed salmon) should be cooked to 170°F to ensure any harmful bacteria have been killed throughout.

Cooking in the Oven

Bacteria can grow slowly in the center of food if the food is cooked in an oven below the minimum temperature of 325°F. Cooking food below 325°F for an extended period of time is a dangerous practice.

Cooking in the Microwave Oven

Covering food with a plastic lid, plastic wrap, or a paper towel captures the steam and allows food to cook thoroughly. The covering should not touch the food but should be vented so steam can escape. Stirring and rotating the container midway through cooking helps distribute heat and steam evenly. A thermometer should be used to check the temperature of the food in multiple spots. After reaching a temperature of 170°F throughout, the food should remain covered for an additional two minutes.

Cleaning Up After Cooking

The cooking area, utensils, and anything that has come in contact with food should be cleaned in the same manner these items are cleaned and sanitized prior to cooking.

Managing Leftovers

Hot foods should be refrigerated within two hours of cooking. Food that has been left standing for more than two hours should be thrown out. No amount of food is worth the risk of acquiring a foodborne illness. It is cheaper to throw out bad food than to pay expensive medical bills or miss work. **When in doubt, throw it out!**

Leftovers should be eaten or frozen within two to three days of being prepared. Store leftovers in small containers to allow for quick cooling (and energy savings) in the refrigerator or freezer. Label them with the cook date so they can be consumed or frozen within a safe amount of time. Labeling leftovers with the date when food was initially prepared will prevent guesswork later.

For freezer storage, products should be tightly wrapped in a freezer-safe container to prevent freezer burn and a possible reduction in quality. For refrigerator storage, hot foods should be quickly cooled (in an ice bath) and consumed as soon as possible (usually within three days for cooked foods). Foods like soups and stews should be refrigerated in shallow containers that are no more than four inches high. This allows the food to cool rapidly.

Stuffing should always be removed from stuffed meats and stored in containers separate from the meat.

Reheated leftovers should be cooked until they are steaming hot or boiling. A food thermometer should be used to confirm that the temperature reaches at least 170°F.

Takeout Food

Everyone likes the convenience of takeout food from time to time. Whether a family meal enjoyed at home or a team lunch at the office, if there are leftovers, safe food-storage and reheating practices still apply. Here are a few basics to keep in mind:

- If a takeout meal is not going to be eaten within two hours, it should be placed in the refrigerator.
- Eat leftover takeout food within two days of purchasing it (assuming it has been properly refrigerated).
- Pizza or other takeout food that has been sitting out for more than two hours should be discarded.
- Some takeout containers, such as Chinese takeout boxes with metal handles and other containers that contain harmful chemicals that food may absorb at high temperatures, are not microwave oven safe. To be safe, always reheat food in microwave-safe glass or ceramic cookware.

Bag Lunches

Whether packing lunch for your school-age kids or for yourself to take to work, you should pack only as much perishable food as can be eaten in one sitting. That way there will be no guessing as to how to safely store leftovers.

Here are some tips for preparing and packing cold or hot lunches that will help ensure a fresh and tasty meal:

- If preparing items that are to be eaten chilled, such as chicken salad or pasta salad, prepare them the night before so they have time to thoroughly chill in the refrigerator.

- Sandwiches can be kept cold by freezing them. However, to maintain the best quality, don't freeze sandwiches that include mayonnaise, lettuce, or tomatoes. Pack those ingredients separately and add them when ready to eat.
- Cold food keeps best in an insulated, soft-sided lunchbox or bag.
- When packing perishable food, remember that a cold source (for example, a frozen gel pack or ice box) should be packed along with it. Perishable food should be discarded shortly after the cold source has thawed, as it can no longer be considered safe to eat.
- If packing foods meant to be eaten hot, such as soup or chili, use an insulated container. The food must stay at 140°F or above to remain safe, so the container should be kept closed until lunchtime.
- Food being reheated in a microwave oven should be covered to retain moisture and create even heating, and it should reach a minimum temperature of 165°F (steaming hot).
- Lunchboxes and reusable bags should be cleaned and sanitized on a regular basis. Fabric bags ideally should be machine-washable; metal or plastic lunchboxes should be dishwasher-safe.

PART VIII
HOLIDAY FOOD SAFETY

Holiday Food Safety

Holidays are a great time for bringing together family and friends and enjoying large quantities of home-cooked food. It's important to pay close attention to food quality, handling, and preparation during these exciting and hectic times. And planning ahead can help ensure safe and stress-free entertaining.

Below are some helpful hints that can make the holidays enjoyable and safe.

Ham

While most hams have been cured (e.g., smoked, aged, or dried), they can still be carriers of foodborne bacteria. To be safe, follow these tips:

- Always check the label, as most canned hams require refrigeration.
- If refrigeration is required, store sliced or whole ham above raw meats and seafood.
- Use slices within three to four days and a whole ham within a week.
- Use cooked ham portions that come prewrapped from the store within three to five days.
- Adhere to "use by" dates on hams sealed at the factory.
- If freezing ham, wrap it in a plastic freezer bag or freezer paper, and use it within one or two months as ham tends to lose flavor and texture once stored in the freezer.
- Fresh ham and other fresh pork should be cooked to a temperature of 160°F.

- Ham that is labeled "fully cooked" may be served either hot or cold.
- If reheating ham, heat it to 165°F.

Turkey

There are many things to consider in preparing and cooking a turkey. The information below will guide you through the steps of purchasing, thawing, and cooking a great-tasting bird.

Purchasing

- As a rule of thumb, 1¼ pounds of turkey should be purchased for each diner. This translates into a 10-pound turkey for a party of eight.
- If leftovers are desired for future meals, purchase a bigger bird (more pounds per person).
- Purchasing a fresh turkey two to three days prior to cooking will avoid the inconvenience of thawing.

Refrigerator Thaw-Time Guide

To thaw a whole frozen turkey in the refrigerator (the safest way), plan on about 24 hours of thawing per five pounds of turkey. Below is a thaw-time guide:

8-12 pounds	1-2 days
12-16 pounds	2-3 days
16-20 pounds	3-4 days
20-24 pounds	4-5 days

In-Water Thaw-Time Guide

- To thaw a whole frozen turkey in water, plan on about 30 minutes per pound.
- If a turkey is thawed in water, no part of it should remain in the Danger Zone (between 40°–140°F) for more than two hours.
- The sink should be filled with cold water, and the water should be changed every 30 minutes.

Here is a thaw-time guide:

8-12 pounds	4-6 hours
12-16 pounds	6-8 hours
16-20 pounds	8-10 hours
20-24 pounds	10-12 hours

Thawing in the Microwave Oven

Before thawing a turkey in a microwave oven, check the manufacturer's instructions for the capacity of the oven, the time required per pound, and the power setting.

All metal (sometimes used to hold the legs together) must be removed from the turkey before it is placed in a microwave oven, as metal placed inside a microwave oven can cause a fire.

Cooking a Turkey

Given the size of most turkeys, proper cooking can be tricky. Following a few basic steps will help ensure a well-cooked, juicy, and tasty turkey.

- The turkey should be placed in a shallow roasting pan, breast up, and the oven temperature should never be set lower than 325°F.
- The turkey will be done and safe to eat when the meat thermometer reads at least 165°F in the thigh meat (the thermometer should not touch the bone).
- Juices should be clear, not bloody.
- If the bird is cooked with stuffing inside it, the center of the stuffing should reach 165°F.

Safe Stuffing

The USDA does not recommend cooking stuffing inside a turkey. Due to the large size of a whole turkey, it is difficult for heat to penetrate the bird at a fast rate while cooking. Therefore, the safest way to prepare stuffing is to cook it outside the bird. If stuffing is placed in a cold turkey and it is cooked slowly, dangerous bacteria can begin to produce toxins in the stuffing while the outside of the turkey is heating up. This creates a potentially dangerous situation.

Recommended cooking times for turkeys:	
Unstuffed	
8-12 pounds	2¾-3 hours
12-14 pounds	3-3¾ hours
14-18 pounds	3¾-4¼ hours
18-20 pounds	4¼-4½ hours

Recommended cooking times for turkeys:	
Stuffed	
8-12 pounds	3-3½ hours
12-14 pounds	3½-4 hours
14-18 pounds	4-4½ hours
18-20 pounds	4¼-4¾ hours
20-24 pounds	4¾-5¼ hours

However, if you choose to cook stuffing inside a turkey, the stuffing should be packed loosely and heated to 170°F, and the recommended cooking directions/times listed in the preceding charts should be followed.

Roasts

Holiday dinners don't only have to be about turkey and ham. There are several types of roasted meats you may wish to serve. Use these guidelines when preparing roasts:

- The meat should be placed in a shallow, uncovered pan on the oven rack at 325°F. This method will help keep the meat tender while minimizing shrinkage due to moisture evaporation. (The USDA advises against cooking meat at temperatures below 325°F, as this can cause it to remain in the Danger Zone [between 40°–140°F] too long.)

- Rolled and deboned cuts of meat need more time to cook per pound than bone-in meats as it takes longer for heat to penetrate solid meat.
- Scored, rolled, or tenderized meats should be cooked to an internal temperature of 160°F.
- Fat content affects meat's cooking time, so use a food thermometer to monitor the internal temperature of the roast and avoid overcooking it.

Serving at Holiday Parties

Two hours is the maximum time food can safely be kept out without refrigeration.

Storing and Reheating Leftovers

As a general rule, meat should be stored separately from other foods due to its high propensity for contamination. Therefore, leftover turkey, stuffing, and gravy should all be stored separately. Before the turkey is put away, all the meat should be removed from the bone and refrigerated in shallow containers. This should happen within two hours of cooking. Leftover turkey and stuffing should be used within three to four days; use gravy within one to two days. Leftovers can be kept around longer if they are frozen. When leftovers are reheated, they should be heated to 165°F.

Eggs Safety During Easter and the Holiday Season

Easter season has a special food safety concern—egg hunts! After an egg is cooked, the shell may crack, and it is possible for harmful bacteria to get inside. Raw eggs sometimes contain salmonella bacteria inside the shell, and they can be potentially hazardous if not refrigerated or completely cooked. Like any other cooked food, a cooked egg needs to be handled safely.

When hiding cooked eggs, place them in spots free of dirt, pets, or other things that might contaminate the eggs. From a timing perspective, make sure the eggs are not in the Danger Zone (40°-140°F) for more than two hours. After they are found, place them in the refrigerator. The best practice during the Easter season is to use plastic eggs for the egg hunt and keep the real eggs in the refrigerator.

If blowing out yokes for painting empty shells, remember that the yokes may contain salmonella bacteria and should not be consumed.

Making eggnog is a special holiday tradition for many families. An eggnog mixture made from raw eggs should be cooked or heated in a microwave oven to 160°F or until it thickens enough to coat a spoon, then refrigerated immediately. Pasteurized eggs are used in commercial eggnog, so cooking is not required. Homemade eggnog using egg substitutes is also safe since these commercial products have been pasteurized.

Homemade holiday desserts made with eggs can be harmful if proper precautions are not taken. High temperatures are required to cook recipes such as cakes, cookies, and candies that include raw eggs. Raw eggs in homemade cookie dough and cake batter may present a hazard, so avoid consumption (licking the bowl) until the latter are fully cooked. Egg substitutes eliminate the hazards associated with raw eggs so are therefore a safe alternative.

Mail Order Foods

Mail order food gifts, such as cooked or salted hams, cheeses, sausages, and chocolates, make popular holiday presents and oftentimes arrive unrefrigerated. If a food item that is shelf-stable (like crackers, candy, or canned food) is received, there should be no concern about safety when kept at room temperature. However, do check the package for any damage, and ensure that cans do not bulge, leak, or have large dents. If they do, they should be returned to the manufacturer.

Some foods come with a label stating "keep refrigerated." This indicates that the food product may have bacteria inside that can grow to hazardous levels if not properly refrigerated. A salt-cured ham (country ham), however, is different; the manufacturer has preserved it by adding high levels of salt (potentially harmful bacteria will not grow in the presence of high levels of salt). It is normally safe to keep a salted ham at room temperature; however, it should be refrigerated or frozen for added safety.

Foods such as sausage, soft cheeses, and unsalted hams are not cooked at high enough temperatures to rid them of potentially harmful bacteria, so they must be kept refrigerated. However, some of these foods may contain additives that make them shelf-stable. The best practice is to read the label to see how the food should be safely stored. Call the manufacturer or shipping company if any questions or concerns arise.

When purchasing mail order food products, inquire about how the food will be packaged and shipped. If the food is perishable, as in the case of meat or poultry, it must be kept cold during shipping. With overnight delivery service, food can be safely packed and shipped almost anywhere in the world and still arrive cold or frozen.

The sender may not want to spoil the surprise of a food gift arriving by mail; however, it is a good idea to let the recipients know if a perishable gift is on its way so they can be on the lookout and prepared to immediately refrigerate it.

Receiving Mail Order Food

When food marked "keep refrigerated" is received, it should be opened immediately and the temperature should be checked. It should be frozen or partially frozen with ice crystals still visible or, at minimum, refrigerator-cold to the touch. Refrigerate or freeze the food immediately; it is always safe to refreeze the product, although the taste and texture might be affected.

If the food arrives warm, notify the company about getting a replacement product or a refund. Do not eat "keep refrigerated" food that arrives warm! It is the company's responsibility to deliver perishable foods on time and in a safely edible condition; the sender's concern should be to ensure that someone is home to receive the package.

While mail order food is often yummy and enticing, do not

eat it if the food has not been transported and stored at proper temperatures. **When in doubt, throw it out!** (Or return it to the sender.)

Storing Mail Order Food

Before storing mail order food, always read the manufacturer's directions relating to the proper storage procedures.

Canned Meat: Refrigerate if indicated on the label. Unopened products are usually shelf-stable for two to five years.

Note: Do not freeze canned food, as the can may burst.

Hard Cheese: Store at room temperature or refrigerate to extend the quality.

"Cook Before Eating" Ham: Refrigerate for up to one week.

Country Ham: Shelf-stable for one year if unsliced. May be refrigerated for two to three months if sliced.

Game Birds: Refrigerate for no more than two days raw.

Hard or Dry Sausage: If unopened, it can be kept in the cupboard or pantry for four to six weeks or in the refrigerator for six months. After opening, it can be stored for up to three weeks in the refrigerator.

"Keep Refrigerated" Sausage: Store in the refrigerator for up to one week.

Sending/Shipping Perishable Food From Home

The best way to prepare food for shipment is to freeze it solid first. While the food is still frozen, place it in a Styrofoam box with a cold source (solid dry ice is best) next to the food. Fill up the empty space in the box with paper or foam "popcorn." If there is a great deal of air space in the box, the ice will thaw more rapidly. Finally, clearly label the package with "Perishable Food - Keep Refrigerated." Ship the package utilizing an overnight delivery service, and let the recipient know when to expect delivery. If no one is home during the day, the package should be shipped to an office address, or a neighbor should be notified to receive the package. The goal is to make sure that the recipient receives the food at or below 40°F.

How to Host a Safe Party

When hosting a party, remember it is your responsibility to ensure the safety and well-being of your guests. Advance planning and attention to proper food service are essential. Here are some basic guidelines to help keep your guests safe, happy, and well-fed:

- Put food out in small quantities, and replenish it throughout the duration of the party.
- Keep cold food cold and hot food hot until it is served.
- Keep cold food on ice and hot food in food warmers throughout the party.
- Always discard cut produce that has been out of the refrigerator for more than four hours (when veggie trays are replenished, discard items that are nearing

the four-hour limit). The four hours includes preparation, transport, and serving time.

- Provide serving spoons with candy dishes and nut dishes so people do not put their fingers into the bowl. Dirty fingers in a nut dish or candy dish can cause a great deal of problems for a large number of people.

- For catered parties, always hire a company that has a current license from a local or state regulatory authority. This ensures that the catering company is inspected on a periodic basis to determine if it is safely preparing and handling food. Ask to see the license before a contract is signed.

Camping, Picnics, and Traveling

When traveling with food or going on a picnic or camping trip, there are many opportunities for perishables to become exposed to warm temperatures that bacteria love. To ensure that everyone has a great time, follow some basic food safety rules.

Food Storage

Coolers and Containers

Transporting food starts with the proper containers and coolers, and with the proper cooling method. Here are several suggestions for packing and handling coolers to help keep your food cool, fresh, and safe:

- Whenever possible, choose a plastic, fiberglass, or steel cooler. They are more durable than Styrofoam coolers and can better resist outdoor wear.
- Make sure the cooler has enough ice to keep food at 40°F or less. Large blocks of ice will keep food colder longer than cubed or crushed ice. Use clean, empty milk cartons to prefreeze blocks of ice, or use frozen gel packs.
- A full cooler will maintain its cold temperature longer than one that is only partially filled. Pack any remaining space with additional ice or with fruit and nonperishable food.
- If possible, transport the cooler in the coolest part of the car. For example, during summer months don't transport the cooler in the trunk where there is no air conditioning.

- Whenever possible, keep the cooler in the shade, under an umbrella, covered with a blanket or, if the picnic is at the beach, partially buried in the sand.
- Keep the cooler lid closed as much as possible, and replenish the ice as needed.
- Use separate coolers for drinks and nonperishable food so that the cooler containing perishable food will not have to be opened and closed as often.
- Store food in watertight containers to prevent contact with melting ice.
- Securely wrap or bag foods that may drip or leak, particularly raw meat, poultry, or fish.

Perishable Foods

Main meal items are likely to consist of perishable foods. A little advance planning will go a long way toward making sure perishables remain viable, minimizing food waste, and avoiding potential health hazards.

- Pack perishable foods directly from the refrigerator into the cooler. Place the food that will be used first in the cooler last. Pack meat, poultry, and fish while they are still frozen.
- Attempt to keep perishable foods inside the cooler as much as possible.
- When serving food in temperatures above 90°F, limit the time that perishable foods sit out to one hour or less.
- Try to take the right amount of food so storing leftovers will not be an issue.
- If there is still ice in the cooler when you get home and the food was not in the Danger Zone (between 40°–140°F) for more than two hours, the food is okay

to save. If the cold source has melted or is only cool, discard all perishables in the cooler.

Nonperishable Foods

In addition to perishable foods, the picnic should include an assortment of nonperishable foods, such as fresh fruits and vegetables, nuts, trail mix, potato chips, crackers, peanut butter, and jelly.

Beverages

If potable water (safe drinking water) is not available at the picnic or camping spot, then bottled water should be included with the food and beverages.

Hot Foods

Hot foods are also highly perishable. Observe these safety guidelines for transporting and holding them:

- Transport hot foods in an insulated chest, and keep them hot until they are consumed.
- Hot food that has been held below 140°F for more than two hours (including transportation time and serving time) may not be safe to eat and should be discarded.

Grilling

Many picnics and camping trips include cooking food on an open grill. This practice comes with its own set of safety measures.

- When grilling, remove from the cooler only the amount of meat that will fit on the grill at one time.
- Do not partially grill meat for use later. When cooking any type of meat, cook it until it is completely done to ensure that harmful bacteria are killed.
- When food is taken off the grill, place it on a clean plate; do not place grilled items on a plate that held raw meat.
- Place leftover food in the cooler promptly after grilling or serving.

Clean Hands and Utensils

A day spent in the great outdoors can be quite invigorating. However, it also has the potential to expose us to an array of bacteria and germs. Maintaining cleanliness of hands and work surfaces when preparing and consuming food outdoors can mean the difference between a fun outing and a bout with foodborne illness. Keep these tips in mind:

- Wash and sanitize hands and work areas with soap and warm water or disposable hand wipes before serving or eating food, and make sure that all utensils are clean and sanitized before preparing food.
- If potable water is not available and the bottled water supply is limited, disposable wipes should be used to clean hands when working with food.
- When using soap to clean cookware and utensils, wash the pots at camp, not at the water's edge. Dump dirty water on dry ground, far away from fresh water. Soap is not good for rivers and streams.

Rugged Camping

For persons who are hiking or camping without the ability to transport perishable foods, advances in food packaging technology have produced many relatively lightweight foods that do not require refrigeration. These include peanut butter in plastic jars; concentrated juice in boxes; canned tuna, ham, chicken, and beef; dried noodles and soups; beef jerky and other dried meats; dehydrated foods; dried fruits and nuts; and powdered milk and fruit drinks.

Whenever possible, bottled water should be packed for drinking and/or mixing with food. Always assume that the water in streams and rivers is not safe to drink. For camping in remote areas, purchase commercial purification tablets or equipment, and learn purification techniques.

Leftover food should be burned, not dumped; it may be harmful to wildlife and also may attract unwanted wild visitors to your campsite.

Storing Caught Fin Fish

If an outing includes fishing, it is important to properly store the day's catch. Here are some tips for handling fin fish:

- Wrap whole and cleaned fish in watertight plastic bags and store them on ice.
- Keep three to four inches of ice on the bottom of the cooler, and alternate layers of fish and ice.
- Store coolers out of the sun, and cover them with a blanket.
- Once home, eat fresh fish in one to two days, or freeze for long-term storage.

Storing Caught Shellfish

A catch of shellfish requires a special set of procedures for storing and cooking. The following are a few of the most important points to remember:

- Only catch molluskan shellfish (oysters, clams, and mussels) from waters that have been approved by public health authorities.
- For safety reasons, crabs, lobsters, and other shellfish must be kept alive until cooked.
- Store them in live wells or out of water in a bushel or laundry basket under wet burlap.
- Live oysters should be cooked within seven to 10 days; mussels and clams should be cooked within four to five days.

Guidelines When Traveling Abroad

Food Safety

According to the Centers for Disease Control and Prevention (CDC), travelers' diarrhea (TD) is the most common form of foodborne illness, affecting between 20 percent and 50 percent of international travelers (an estimated 10 million people) each year. Understanding the potential hazards of consuming certain organisms and chemicals while traveling abroad will go a long way to ensure healthy, illness-free travel.

Water quality for drinking, brushing teeth, and washing fruits and vegetables may not be safe when outside the United States. To see a list of countries with safe drinking water, visit neomam.com/blog/tap-water and read A *Traveler's Guide to Safe Tap Water.*

Many countries have safe food practices; however, the World Health Organization (WHO) guidelines should always be closely adhered to when traveling abroad. Refer to www.who.int for current guidelines.

In general, adhere to the following recommendations to minimize the risk of acquiring unwanted bacterial, viral, or parasitic infection:

- Steer clear of undercooked or uncooked foods, especially red meat, poultry, pork, eggs, or seafood.
- Do not consume food from street vendors or restaurants and markets that appear unclean or do not offer proper refrigeration.
- Ensure that fruits and vegetable are properly washed in clean water (observe this process!). Fruits and vegetables with a peel that is removed before eating (bananas, mangos, watermelon, citrus) are the safest options. Likewise, avoid salads made with uncooked fruits and vegetables.
- Drink and brush teeth with bottled water or water boiled in an effort to kill germs.
- Avoid ice in drinks as the water used to make the ice may be contaminated.
- Pasteurization is the heating process that destroys disease-causing microbes. Therefore, avoid any dairy product (milk, cheese, butter, sour cream, yogurt, etc.) made from unpasteurized milk, and avoid unpasteurized fruit juices.
- Foods labeled "ready to eat" (e.g., packaged sandwiches, potato salad, and coleslaw) should be carefully

inspected for proper refrigeration and cleanliness.
- Avoid large fish from reef areas, as they have the tendency to accumulate chemical toxins.

Best Bets

Granola bars, crackers, candy, sports energy bars, bottled water, and sports drinks are great options for foods that travel well and can be packed from home. Here is a list of foods you can purchase locally that should not pose a health risk:

- Thermally processed foods that have been canned, bottled, or pasteurized.
- Baked goods such as breads and tortillas, which generally do not allow disease-causing bacteria to grow or survive.
- Well-cooked foods that are served extremely hot.
- Bottled water and canned soda.
- Water treated with purification tablets.

Immunizations

Prior to any international travel, contact the U.S. Centers for Disease Control and Prevention (www.cdc.gov or 888-232-3228) for information on:

- The CDC's requirements and recommendations relating to immunizations. Check this at least three months prior to travel so any needed vaccinations can be scheduled and inoculation will have time to take effect.
- Health risks in each country planned for travel.

PART X
FOODBORNE
ILLNESS

Understanding Foodborne Illness (Food Poisoning)

This discussion should be viewed as a guide to the initial treatment of foodborne illness. If serious underlying medical conditions (diabetes, kidney disease, heart problems, immune deficiency, etc.) are present, a physician should be consulted at the onset of foodborne illness. For persons with no medical conditions, if the condition does not improve within 24 hours, or if the condition worsens after 24 hours, a physician should be consulted. Patients and physicians should report foodborne illness, including where the food was purchased, to their local health department.

The Centers for Disease Control and Prevention (CDC) and the World Health Organization (WHO) firmly believe in educating and providing useful resources to the general public to address one of their primary concerns: the safety and security of food and the overall prevention of foodborne illnesses and food poisoning. Yearly, these organizations collect data from different sources throughout the world to compile a variety of data reports to raise awareness of potential food-related issues.

Because many cases of foodborne illness and food poisoning are never reported, exact figures are not known. However, the CDC estimates that each year roughly 1 in 6 Americans (or 48 million people) get sick, 128,000 are hospitalized, and 3,000 die of foodborne diseases. The annual economic impact of foodborne illnesses in the U.S. alone is estimated to be in the billions of dollars. This includes costs for lost wages, medical care, lost business, lower productivity, and legal expenses.

The U.S. government has created strict regulations designed to make the American food supply safe. However, ultimately consumers are responsible for the safety of their food once they are home.

What Is Foodborne Illness?

Ingesting food or beverage that has been contaminated by viruses, pathogenic (disease-producing) bacteria, chemicals or natural toxins (poisons), parasites, or mycotoxins can result in foodborne illness. We use the term "can" because it depends on which contaminant and the amount of the contaminant ingested whether or not symptoms will develop.

Many consumers use the term 'food poisoning' when referring to foodborne illness. However, food poisoning is a specific type of foodborne illness that is caused by ingesting preformed toxins, such as eating improperly stored soup in which bacteria have produced toxins.

Foodborne illness is not to be confused with gastroenteritis. They both result in similar symptoms including nausea, abdominal discomfort, fever, and diarrhea; but gastroenteritis is often accompanied by muscle and joint aches.

Gastroenteritis means that the gastro (stomach) and the entero (intestine) are swollen or irritated. The irritated intestinal mucosa cannot properly absorb nutrients, and the intestinal lining continues to secrete fluid, resulting in dehydration and serious imbalance of important chemicals such as potassium, sodium, and magnesium, as well as in water depletion.

In both food poisoning and gastroenteritis, the vomiting and diarrhea help get rid of the offending germ or toxin. Another weapon in the fight is to generate heat (fever), which creates a hostile environment for invading organisms while also increasing the body's fluid requirements. This, in turn, aggravates the dehydration.

One of the differences between food poisoning and gastroenteritis is that gastroenteritis is usually the result of direct person-to-person transmission of viruses, or transmission from contaminated food or beverage from an infected individual.

The common viruses that cause gastroenteritis are entero-viruses, norovirus, rotavirus, hepatitis A, and hepatitis E. These viruses are the ones that often cause massive illness on cruise ships. Less commonly, gastroenteritis can be caused by bacterial infections and/or toxins elaborated by bacteria and then transmitted from person to person.

Primary Cause

A primary cause of foodborne illness is consumption of foods containing high levels of bacteria. Bacteria alone are not enough to cause illness. However, when protein-rich/high-moisture foods such as meat, fish, poultry, dairy products, cooked vegetables, and eggs (hereafter referred to as perishable foods) are left at temperatures between 40°–140°F (the "Danger Zone") for more than two hours, bacteria are able to multiply to dangerous levels, often resulting in food poisoning.

Other causes of food poisoning include viral, natural toxins, and chemical contamination (chemicals that have been accidentally or purposely added to food).

Treatment

In most healthy people, food poisoning is a self-limiting illness; the body reacts with fever, vomiting, and diarrhea to get rid of the poison, and a full recovery occurs after two to four days.

The treatment for the most common types of minor food poisoning is to replace lost fluids and salts (electrolytes). Adults should consume sports drinks (Gatorade, Powerade), decaffeinated sodas (7-Up, ginger ale, Sprite), and water to replace lost fluids. However, if diarrhea is severe, an oral rehydration solution such as Ceralyte, Pedialyte, or Oralyte should be consumed to replace the fluid losses and prevent dehydration. Sports drinks do not correctly replace the losses in severe cases of diarrhea. Infants and children should be given Pedialyte or Lytren to rehydrate. Nausea can be treated with over-the-counter medications such as Emetrol. Diarrhea can be treated with Immodium or Pepto-Bismol for a short period of time.

Common Types of Foodborne Illness

Much of the information in this section is excerpted from the Centers for Disease Control website at www.cdc.gov.

Bacillus cereus

Common sources: A variety of foods, particularly rice and leftovers, as well as sauces, soups, and other prepared foods that have sat out too long at room temperature

Symptoms appear within: 30 mins.-6 hours (vomiting) 6-15 hours (diarrhea)

Duration: 24 hours

Symptoms: Watery diarrhea, abdominal cramps, nausea, and vomiting

Botulism

Common sources: Home-canned foods with a low acid content, improperly canned commercial foods, home-canned or fermented fish, herb-infused oils, baked potatoes in aluminum foil, cheese sauce, bottled garlic, foods held warm for extended periods of time; for infants: honey, home-canned vegetables and fruits, corn syrup

Symptoms appear within: Infants: 3-30 days Children and adults: 12-72 hours

Duration:	Variable
Symptoms:	Infants: lethargy, weakness, poor feeding, constipation, poor head control, poor gag and sucking reflex
Children and adults:	Double vision, blurred vision, drooping eyelids, slurred speech, difficulty swallowing, dry mouth, muscle weakness

Campylobacter jejuni

Common sources:	Raw or undercooked meat and poultry, unpasteurized milk, and contaminated food and water
Symptoms appear within:	2-5 days, with a range of 1-10 days
Duration:	2-10 days
Symptoms:	Fever, headache, and muscle pain followed by nausea, abdominal pain, and diarrhea
Note:	The most common cause of diarrhea caused by bacteria

Clostridium perfringens

Common sources:	Beef, poultry, gravies
Symptoms appear within:	6-24 hours
Duration:	24 hours or less; in severe cases, symptoms may last for 1-2 weeks
Symptoms:	Diarrhea and abdominal cramps (no fever or vomiting)

Cryptosporidium

Common sources:	Contaminated food and water, unpasteurized beverages (apple cider) contaminated with animal manure; outbreaks have been associated with childcare centers, swimming pools, and lakes; person-to-person and fecal-oral transmission
Symptoms appear within:	1-12 days, with an average of 7 days
Duration:	Up to several weeks after symptoms resolve
Symptoms:	Diarrhea, cramping, abdominal pain; general malaise, fever, anorexia, nausea, and vomiting occur less often; asymptomatic infections are common

Escherichia coli O157:H7 (E. coli) and other enterohemorrhagic strains

Common sources:	Raw or rare ground beef, unpasteurized milk, contaminated water or produce, and dirty hands
Symptoms appear within:	1-10 days
Duration:	Up to 10 days
Symptoms:	Severe abdominal cramps followed by diarrhea, nausea, vomiting, and occasionally

a low-grade fever; compli-
cation is hemolytic uremic
syndrome (HUS) in children

Hepatitis A

Common sources:	Raw or undercooked shellfish from contaminated waters, raw produce, contaminated drinking water, uncooked foods, and cooked foods that are not reheated after contact with an infected food handler
Symptoms appear within:	Average 28 days (ranges 15-50 days)
Duration:	2 weeks - 3 months
Symptoms:	Diarrhea, dark urine, jaundice, fever, headache, nausea, abdominal pain, and loss of appetite

Listeria monocytogenes

Common sources:	Milk, leafy vegetables, unpasteurized dairy products (especially soft cheeses), processed ready-to-eat meats and sandwiches, hot dogs, poultry, refrigerated smoked seafood, refrigerated pâtés, and meat spreads
Symptoms appear within:	Newborns: less than 7 days (early onset) or 7 or more

	days (late onset), Adults: 3-70 days
Duration:	Variable (days to weeks)
Symptoms:	Sudden onset of flu-like symptoms such as fever, headache, backache, and sometimes abdominal pain and diarrhea; complications can include respiratory distress in newborns, miscarriages, still births, and meningitis

Norovirus (Norwalk Virus)

Common sources:	Produce, shellfish, ready-to-eat foods touched by infected food workers (salads, sandwiches, ice, cookies, fruit), or any other foods contaminated with vomit or feces from an infected person
Symptoms appear within:	12-48 hours
Duration:	1-3 days (can last 4-6 days for young children, older adults, and hospitalized patients)
Symptoms:	Diarrhea (watery and non-bloody), vomiting, nausea, and stomach pain
Note:	According to the CDC, norovirus is the leading cause of domestic foodborne illness. It is responsible for 58 percent of all foodborne illness in the United States where

it is attributed to over 500 deaths each year (mostly among young children and the elderly). The primary source of norovirus comes from infected people who do not wash their hands after using the bathroom. The un-washed hands transmit fecal matter or vomit particles to food or food surfaces. This results in transmitting the virus through food.

Salmonella (Salmonellosis)

Common sources:	Contaminated eggs, poultry, meat, unpasteurized milk or juice, cheese, contaminated raw fruits and vegetables (alfalfa sprouts, melons), spices, and nuts; can spread through cross-contamination
Symptoms appear within:	12-72 hours
Duration:	4-7 days
Symptoms:	Abdominal pain, diarrhea, nausea, chills, fever, and headache
Note:	The second most common cause of foodborne illness

Shigella

Common sources: Contaminated food or water, salads and sandwiches that involve hand contact in their preparation, raw vegetables contaminated in the field, and contact with an infected person

Symptoms appear within: 1-7 days

Duration: 2-7 days

Symptoms: Sudden abdominal cramping, fever, diarrhea that may be bloody or contain mucus, nausea, and vomiting

Staphylococcus aureus (Staph)

Common sources: Found on human skin in cuts, pimples, and in the nose and throat; food sources include cooked foods that are high in protein (ham, eggs, tuna, chicken), salads, bakery products, and dairy products; spread by improper food handling

Symptoms appear within: 30 mins.-7 hours

Duration: 1-2 days

Symptoms: Abdominal pain, nausea, vomiting, and diarrhea; occasionally followed by fever,

weakness, headache, dizzi-
ness, and chills

Vibrio vulnificus/Vibrio parahaemolyticus

Common sources:	Raw or undercooked shell-fish, particularly raw oysters
Symptoms appear within:	V. vulnificus: 1-7 days
	V. parahaemolyticus: 2-48 hours
Duration:	2-8 days
Symptoms:	Diarrhea, vomiting, and abdominal pain in healthy individuals; sudden chills, fever, shock, and skin lesions

Helpful Tips

The following pages include helpful tips you can use to enjoy safe and great-tasting food.

Condiments

MAYONNAISE SAFETY

According to Hellmann's, mayonnaise is NOT a food safety problem! The ingredients in mayonnaise, such as vinegar, lemon juice, and salt, create an unfavorable environment for bacteria that will slow or prevent its growth. However, many of the ingredients typically mixed with mayonnaise, like potatoes, ham, or chicken, have a greater susceptibility to bacterial growth than the mayonnaise itself..

Dairy & Eggs

STORING YOGURT AND SOUR CREAM

Yogurt and sour cream will remain fresh longer if stored upside down on the refrigerator shelf.

MILK

If constantly stored at 38°-40°F, milk can remain fresh for up to five days beyond the shelf-removal date. As a safeguard, be sure the milk smells good before consuming it.

USING RAW EGGS

When raw eggs are used in cake and cookie recipes, the uncooked batter or dough should not be eaten.

Fruits

CHOOSING FRESH BERRIES

Most berries are very fragile and should be inspected carefully when purchased.

CHOOSING GRAPEFRUIT

Pink grapefruit is generally sweeter than white varieties.

CHOOSING ORANGES

Thin-skinned oranges are ideal for juicing. Thick-skinned and blood oranges (with red pulp), including the navel (which is large, seedless, and easy to peel), make the best eating oranges.

CONSUMING KIWIFRUIT

The skin of kiwifruit is edible, but the fruit is usually served peeled.

COOKING WITH QUINCES

Quinces are high in tannins, which help to tenderize meat, so they are a great addition to stews.

JUICING LEMONS

Microwave lemons for ten seconds before cutting them to release more juice.

PURCHASING CARAMBOLA

Carambola, also known as starfruit, should be purchased green and allowed to turn yellow. It is often used as a decorative garnish.

PURCHASING DATES

Avoid buying dates with crystalized sugars.

REFRIGERATING BANANAS

Refrigeration turns banana skins black, but the quality of the fruit is not affected.

RIPENING CANTALOUPES

If cantaloupes are left room temperature, they will soften and become juicier.

RIPENING PEARS

Pears are usually picked for shipping before they have ripened, as the flesh is extremely fragile. Putting a banana or ripe apple in with the fruit helps to speed up ripening. Pears are ripe when the flesh near the stem is slightly soft.

RIPENING SAPODILLA

Wash sapodilla before putting them aside to ripen. The ripening process can take up to nine days.

SELECTING PASSIONFRUIT

Passionfruit is also known as granadilla. The purple type is less acid than the yellow variety.

SELECTING PINEAPPLES

When mature, pineapples are usually dark green, firm, plump, and heavy for their size.

SELECTING AND SERVING GRAPES

Grapes do not ripen after they are picked. Do not get them wet; however, wash them just before serving.

STORING FRESH FIGS

Store fresh figs in separate container away from vegetables. Overripe figs will give off a bad smell.

STORING LEMON JUICE

Fresh lemon juice should be stored in a tightly sealed, tinted bottle to extend its freshness.

STORING PLUMS

Store plums at room temperature until they are ripe, then refrigerate them in a plastic bag.

THE NATURE OF DURIAN

Durian has a naturally very strong, unpleasant odor.

UNDERSTANDING DRAGON FRUIT

Dragon fruit is also known as pitaya. Its flavor is a cross between a kiwi and a pear.

USING GUAVA

Guava may be eaten fresh or used to make preserves.

WASHING STRAWBERRIES

Only wash strawberries right before serving them. Note that strawberries do not ripen after they are picked.

Grain Products

REVIVING STALE GRAIN PRODUCTS

When cereals, crackers, or other grain-based snacks become stale, spread them on a cookie sheet and bake at 425°F for a few minutes. While these foods will regain crispness, it will not help foods that have lost their flavor.

In the Grocery Store

PACKAGE SAFETY

Always discard any package or container that spurts liquid when opened.

SELECTING FOOD ITEMS AT QUICK MARTS

Hot air rises. Cool air falls. Keep this in mind when shopping at quick marts. Products on the lower shelves are typically cooler, fresher, and safer to consume.

In the Kitchen

ELIMINATING FRUIT FLIES

Apple cider vinegar also works as an effective trap for pesky fruit flies. Simply pour about an inch of vinegar into a glass, add a few dots of dishwashing soap, cover with clear plastic wrap or a plastic baggie (secure with a rubber band if necessary), and punch a few tiny holes in the plastic (a toothpick works well). The flies will be lured in by the fruity aroma, and the soap will help prevent their escape.

HYDROGEN PEROXIDE AND VINEGAR SOLUTION

An effective homemade cleaning solution is a combination of hydrogen peroxide and vinegar (apple cider or white). Keep each in its own spray bottle and apply equal amounts to the surface to be cleaned. Let the solution sit for five minutes to completely sanitize, then wipe dry.

LUNCHBOXES AND TOTES

Lunchboxes and tote bags should be washed after each use. Fabric bags ideally should be machine-washable; metal or plastic lunchboxes should be dishwasher-safe.

SETTING REFRIGERATOR TEMPERATURE

Keeping the refrigerator temperature too low can be expensive. A reading of 26°-30°F can increase energy consumption by as much as 25 percent.

Meats

STORING HAMBURGER MEAT

If hamburger meat is purchased on Monday and the plan is to freeze it, then it should be placed directly in the freezer when it arrives home from the grocery store. It is not a good idea to wait until Tuesday or Wednesday before placing it in the freezer.

Poultry

THAWING A FROZEN BIRD IN THE FRIDGE

Thaw a frozen bird (turkey, chicken, game hen, etc.) in the refrigerator to ensure even and safe cooking.

Vegetables

ASSESSING THE QUALITY OF HERBS

The quality of both fresh and dried herbs can be best assessed by their aroma. You can test them by crumbling a few leaves between your fingers and then smelling the leaves. A strong aroma indicates good quality.

COOKING GREENS

Greens cook down considerably, to one-quarter or less of their original volume.

CONSUMING SUMMER SQUASH

The rind and seeds of summer squash are also edible.

GAUGING CAULIFLOWER FRESHNESS

Old cauliflower gives off a strong taste and smell.

HANDLING SWEET POTATOES

Sweet potatoes bruise and discolor easily and should be handled with care.

KEEPING HERBS FRESH

To keep parsley and cilantro fresh for up to a week, first trim the stems, then stand the bunches in a glass with a few inches of water, place them in the refrigerator, and cover the tops with a plastic baggie. Do not wash until ready to use.

KEEPING MUSHROOMS FRESH

Mushrooms are highly perishable. Store them in a paper, not a plastic, bag, and wash them only right before use.

PREPARING BOK CHOY

Chop an inch off the stalk of bok choy before washing.

PREPARING TURNIPS

Turnips need to be scrubbed but not peeled before eating.

PREPPING ROOT VEGETABLES FOR STORAGE

Remove tops from beets, carrots, and radishes before storing.

STORING ARTICHOKES

Sprinkle artichokes with water before storing.

STORING BASIL

Fresh basil likes it warm and stores best on the counter in a few inches of water and loosely covered with a plastic baggie.

STORING ONIONS

Although onions and potatoes are both best stored outside of the refrigerator in a cool, dry, dark place, they should always be stored separately as onions cause potatoes to sprout.

STORING POTATOES

Avoid storing potatoes in the refrigerator as this may alter the taste. Also, a bitter taste may be created when potatoes are stored in the light. For best results, store potatoes in a paper bag in a dry, cool place.

STORING TOMATOES (CUT)

Cut tomatoes should be refrigerated, even though refrigeration will alter the taste.

STORING TOMATOES (WHOLE)

When storing tomatoes, place them stem side down in a single layer. This will allow them breathing room and prevent bruising.

USING ASPARAGUS

Use asparagus quickly; there is no benefit from extended storage.

USING FROZEN GINGER

To use frozen ginger, slice off a piece of the unthawed root, then rewrap the unused portion and return to freezer.

USING GREEN ONIONS

Use green onions as soon as possible after purchase as they are fairly perishable.

Afterword

We hope you have enjoyed the material presented in this book. Our objective was to present the most useful information possible regarding the important topic of food safety and quality, not only to help protect readers from the risk of foodborne illness but also to offer knowledge that can enrich their daily lives as relates to food.

Hopefully, *The Food Safety Book* will serve as your reference tool of choice for everyday questions concerning food safety, quality, selection, storage, preparation, and consumption. Here's to healthy, happy, and safe eating!

Index

beans: canned, 76, 99; dried, 99; green, 47, 75, 97; snap, 47, 97; wax, 47, 97

bear meat, 131

beef: as source of foodborne illness, 167, 168; corned, 91; fresh, 90, 125; ground, 125; jerky, 156; minimum cooking temperature, 129

beets: canned, 76; fresh 47, 72, 97, 183

berries, 27, 86, 95, 176. See also individual entries

beverages: as source of foodborne illness, 167; bottled water, 154; fruit, 92; rice, 92; soda, 104; soy, 93; sports, 159, 165

biscuits, 89, 103

boar meat, 131

bok choy, 48, 97, 183

botulism, 127, 166

bouillon cubes/granules, 99

bread: commercial, 84, 159; dough, 86; flat, 84; mix, 103; pita, 85; rolls, 85

broccoli, 48-49, 75, 97

brownie mix, 103

Brussels sprouts, 49, 75, 97

burritos, frozen, 86

butter, 87, 158

buttermilk, 87

C
—

cabbage, 49, 71, 75, 97

cage-free eggs, 13-14

cake, 84, 85; mix, 103

camping, 152-157

candy, 99, 145, 159

canned food: as source of foodborne illness, 166; storing, 68, 75-77, 99, 100, 145, 147, 156; shopping for, 10

cantaloupe, 27-28, 74, 95, 177

coolers, 20, 79, 152-154, 156
corn: canned, 99; on the cob, 51-52, 97
corn syrup, 103; as source of foodborne illness, 166
corned beef, 91
cornmeal, 103
cornstarch, 103
crab, 94; minimum cooking temperature, 129-130; storing,
    157
crackers, 68, 100, 145, 154, 159, 179
crayfish, 94
cream, fresh, 70, 88
crisper, refrigerator, 71
croissant, 84
cucumbers, 52, 97
cutting boards, 113-114; sanitizing, 3, 110, 112, 113

D
—

dairy: organic, 19; product dating, 9, 10, 11; selecting, 18; stor-
    ing, 68, 70, 87-88
dates, 30-31, 95, 177
deer meat, 131
deli foods, 18-19, 69, 89
diarrhea: as symptom of foodborne illness, 157, 163, 164, 165,
    166, 167, 168, 169, 170, 171, 172, 173
dips, 70; sour-cream-based, 92
doughnuts, 85
dragon fruit, 31, 95, 179
duck, 93; minimum cooking temperature, 129
durian, 31-32, 95, 179

E
—

E. coli, 168

L

lamb, 91, 125; minimum cooking temperature, 129
leafy vegetables, 71, 72; as source of foodborne illness, 169
leeks, 55, 98
leftovers: as source of foodborne illness, 165; disposing of,
    156; reheating, 132, 143; storing, 77, 133, 134, 155
lemon juice, 104, 177, 178
lemons, 36, 96
lentils, dried, 100
lettuce, 71, 72, 75; iceberg, 55, 98; leaf, 56, 98; packaged, 56,
    98; romaine, 56-57, 98
limes, 36, 96
listeria, 169
liver, 91
lobster, 86, 94, 129; minimum cooking temperature, 130;
    storing, 157
lunch meats, 92, 93, 94
lunchboxes, 115, 135, 181
lychees, 36-37, 96

M

mail order foods, 145-147
mangos, 37, 74, 96, 158
mangosteen, 37, 74, 96
margarine, 92
marinating, 120
marshmallow crème, 100
marshmallows, 100
mayonnaise, 68, 74, 105, 135, 175
meat, 89, 90-92; as source of foodborne illness, 164, 167,
    169, 172; canned, 76, 99, 147; cooking frozen, 119; cross-
    contamination, preventing, 18, 68, 70, 112, 113, 118; grilling,

References

The authors would like to recognize the following organizations and websites for contributing information to this book:

About Food
homecooking.about.com/od/foodstorage/a/gingerstorage.htm (accessed August 29, 2016)

American Association of Meat Processors (AAMP)
www.aamp.com (accessed September 7, 2016)
717.367.1168

American Egg Board
www.aeb.org/foodservice/egg-production (accessed
    August 29, 2016)
www.aeb.org/foodservice/egg-safety-handling (accessed
    September 7, 2016)
847.296.7043

Business Insider
www.businessinsider.com/how-to-tell-when-expired-
    food-is-bad (accessed August 29, 2016)

CNN
www.cnn.com/2013/09/19/health/sell-by-dates-waste-
    food (accessed August 29, 2016)

Centers for Disease Control and Prevention (CDC)
www.cdc.gov/foodborneburden (accessed September 7,
    2016)
www.cdc.gov/foodsafety (accessed September 7, 2016)

Centers for Disease Control and Prevention (CDC) (continued)

www.cdc.gov/handwashing/publications-data-stats.html (accessed August 29, 2016)

www.cdc.gov/handwashing/when-how-handwashing. html (accessed August 29, 2016)

www.cdc.gov/salmonella (accessed September 7, 2016)

wwwnc.cdc.gov/travel (accessed September 7, 2016)

800.232.4636 | TTY: 888.232.6348

Chef's Blade

chefsblade.monster.com/training/articles/878-storing-and-purchasing-fresh (accessed August 29, 2016)

Clemson University Cooperative Extension

www.clemson.edu/extension/hgic/food/food_safety/ handling/hgic3505.html (accessed August 29, 2016)

864.656.3311

Clorox Company

www.clorox.com/cleaning-and-laundry-tips/cleaning/ kitchen/how-to-clean-a-cutting-board (accessed September 7, 2016)

404.363.8300

Consumer Reports

www.consumerreports.org/cro/health/food-safety-and-sustainability-guide (accessed September 7, 2016)

http://www.consumerreports.org/cro/ magazine/2014/05/are-brown-eggs-tastier-and-more-nutritious-than-white-eggs/index.htm (accessed August 29, 2016)

800.333.0663

Cornell University Institute of Food Science
www.foodscience.cals.cornell.edu (accessed September 7,
2016)
607.255.3262

Course Hero
www.coursehero.com/file/12449627/food-safety-activity
(accessed August 29, 2016)

DoItYourself
www.doityourself.com/stry/how-to-harvest-a-quince
(accessed August 29, 2016)

eHow
www.ehow.com/how_5794628_tell-star-fruit-ripe.html
(accessed August 29, 2016)

Eat-By Date
www.eatbydate.com (accessed September 7, 2016)

Eat Right: Academy of Nutrition and Dietetics
www.eatright.org/resources/homefoodsafety (accessed
September 7, 2016)

Egg Safety
www.eggsafety.org (accessed September 7, 2016)

Federal Food Safety Information
www.foodsafety.gov/keep/basics/index.html (accessed
September 7, 2016)

Federal Food Safety Information (continued)
www.foodsafety.gov/keep/charts/index.html (accessed
September 7, 2016)

Fight Bac! Partnership for Food Safety Education
www.fightbac.org/egg-stra-care-for-spring-celebrations
   (accessed September 7, 2016)
www.fightbac.org/food-safety-basics/the-core-four-
   practices (accessed September 7, 2016)
www.fightbac.org/free-resources/
   holidayfoodsafetyresources (accessed September 7,
   2016)
www.fightbac.org/glorious-goodies-to-send-and-receive
   (accessed September 7, 2016)
202.220.0651

Fishwatch: US Seafood Facts (NOAA)
www.fishwatch.gov/eating-seafood/buying-and-
   handling (accessed September 7, 2016)

FIT: Fruit and Vegetable
www.fitorganic.com (accessed September 7, 2016)
800.FIT.WASH

Food Marketing Institute: The Food Keeper (FMI)
www.fmi.org/industry-topics/consumer-affairs/food-
   keeper-food-storage-database (accessed September 7,
   2016)
202.452.8444

Food Product Dating and Storage Times
cals.arizona.edu/pubs/health/az1068.html (accessed
   August 29, 2016)

Food Safety Information Council
foodsafety.asn.au/food-safety-at-home (accessed
   September 7, 2016)
0407.626.688

Hellmann's Mayonnaise
www.hellmanns.com (accessed September 7, 2016)
800.418.3275

HGTV
www.youtube.com/watch?v=tMNLyr_ivWs (accessed
   September 7, 2016)

Iowa Department of Public Health
idph.iowa.gov/A-Z (accessed September 7, 2016)
515.28.7689 | 866.227.9878

Kitchen Companion: Your Safe Food Handbook
www.fsis.usda.gov (accessed September 7, 2016)

National Fisheries Institute: About Seafood
www.aboutseafood.com (accessed September 7, 2016)

National Institute On Aging: Food Safety/Publications
http://www.nia.nih.gov/health/publication/whats-your-
   plate/food-safety (accessed September 7, 2016)
877.696.6775

Office of Disease Prevention and Health Promotion
www.health.gov (accessed September 7, 2016)

Publix: A Guide to Food Storage and Handling
www.publix.com (accessed September 7, 2016)
800.242.1227

Purdue University, Purdue Agriculture
www.ag.purdue.edu (accessed September 7, 2016)
765.494.8256 | 888.398.4636

Rainbow Foods
www.rainbow-foods.org (accessed August 29, 2016)
907.586.6476

Shelf Life Advice
www.shelflifeadvice.com (accessed September 7, 2016)
www.shelflifeadvice.com/content/ethylene-and-
    produce-friends-or-foes (accessed September 7, 2016)

Still Tasty: Your Ultimate Shelf-Life Guide
www.stilltasty.com (accessed September 7, 2016)

Stop Foodborne Illness
www.stopfoodborneillness.org/awareness/what-is-
    foodborne-illness (accessed September 7, 2016)
www.stopfoodborneillness.org/awareness/safe-cooking-
    temperatures-2 (accessed September 7, 2016)
www.stopfoodborneillness.org/awareness/consumer-
    information-fact-sheets-2 (accessed September 7,
    2016)
773.269.6555

The Incredible Edible Egg
www.incredibleegg.org/easter (accessed September 7,
    2016)

The Incredible Edible Egg (continued)
www.incredibleegg.org/eggcyclopedia (accessed
    September 7, 2016)

The Iowa Egg Council
iowaegg.org/education/all-about-the-egg/o (accessed
    August 29, 2016)
515.727.4701

The Public Health and Safety Organization (NSF)
www.nsf.org/consumer-resources/health-and-safety-
tips (accessed September 7, 2016)
800.765.2122

**The University of Arizona, College of Agriculture & Life
Sciences Cooperative Extension**
cals.arizona.edu/pubs/health/az1068.html (accessed
August 29, 2016)

Tropical Fruit Growers of South Florida
www.tfgsf.com (accessed September 7, 2016)
305.247.5727

University of Florida (UF): IFAS Extension
http://edis.ifas.ufl.edu/topic_home_food_safety
(accessed September 7, 2016)
352.392.1991 | 352.392.9084

University of Nebraska Lincoln Extension
extensionpublications.unl.edu/assets/pdf/ec446.pdf
(accessed September 7, 2016)
402.472.2966

University of Nevada Cooperative Extension
www.unce.unr.edu/publications/files/hn/2009/fs0911.
pdf (accessed September 7, 2016)
775.784.7070

U.S. Department of Agriculture (USDA)
www.usda.gov/wps/portal/usda/usdahome (accessed
September 7, 2016)

USDA Food and Nutrition Service

www.fns.usda.gov/ofs/produce-information-sheets
(accessed September 7, 2016)

USDA Food Safety and Inspection Service

www.fsis.usda.gov/wps/portal/fsis/topics/food-safety-
education/get-answers (accessed August 29, 2016)

USDA National Agricultural Library

www.nal.usda.gov (accessed September 7, 2016)
202.720.2791

USDA's Meat and Poultry Hotline

www.fsis.usda.gov/wps/portal/fsis/programs-and-
services/contact-centers/usda-meat-and-poultry-
hotline (accessed September 7, 2016)
800.535.4555

U.S. Food and Drug Administration (FDA)

www.fda.gov/downloads/Food/
FoodborneIllnessContaminants/UCM109315.pdf
(accessed September 7, 2016)
www.fda.gov/forconsumers/consumerupdates/
ucm093704.htm (accessed September 7, 2016)
888.463.6332

Vital Farms

vitalfarms.com/pasture-raised-eggs (accessed August 29,
2016) (accessed September 7, 2016)
877-455-3063

World Health Organization (WHO)

www.who.int/en (accessed September 7, 2016)
41.22.791.21.11

Additional Resources

We encourage you to visit the following websites to learn more about food safety and quality:

Academy of Nutrition and Dietetics
www.eatrightpro.org
800.877.1600 | 312.899.0040

American Beverage Association
www.ameribev.org
202.463.6732

American Dairy Science Association (ADSA)
www.adsa.org
217.356.5146

American Frozen Food Institute
www.affi.org
703.821.0770

ConAgra Foods
www.conagrafoods.com

Culinary Institute of America
www.ciachef.edu
845.452.9600

Florida Fruit & Vegetable Association
www.ffva.com
321.214.5200

Fruit & Spice Park
www.fruitandspicepark.org
305.247.5727

Harvard Health Publications
www.health.harvard.edu
617.495.1000

Health.com
www.health.com/health
800.274.2522

Healthy Canadians/Government of Canada
www.healthycanadians.gc.ca
866.225.0709

Institute of Food Technologists
www.ift.org
312.782.8424

International Association of Food Protection
www.foodprotection.org
515.276.3344 | 800.369.6337

International Food Information Council Foundation
www.foodinsight.org
202.296.6540

Kidshealth From Nemours
www.kidshealth.org

National Cattlemen's Beef Association
www.beef.org
303.694.0305

National Chicken Council
www.nationalchickencouncil.org
202.296.2622

National Milk Producers Federation
www.nmpf.org
703.243.6111

National Pork Producers Council
www.nppc.org
202.347.3600

National Restaurant Association
www.restaurant.org
202.331.5900 | 800.424.5156

National Shellfisheries Association
www.shellfish.org
207.832.6812

North American Meat Institute (NAMI)
www.meatinstitute.org
202.587.4200

Nutrition and You
www.nutrition-and-you.com

Parents Magazine
www.parents.com/pregnancy/my-body/nutrition/a-
    food-guide-for-pregnant-women/

Produce Marketing Association (PMA)
www.pma.com
302.731.2409

Self Nutrition Data: Know What You Eat
nutritiondata.self.com

University of Illinois at Urbana-Champaign
www.aces.illinois.edu
217.333.0460

About the Authors

Joe Kivett

After years of calling his mother each time he had a question related to food safety or quality, Joe began researching the answers for himself. His original mission was to create a chart that outlined how long food products last. While conducting his research, Joe discovered a wealth of food-safety and food-quality information that complemented his food-longevity chart, which led to the creation of this simple guide, written specifically for the consumer.

Before becoming a published author, Kivett worked at Walt Disney Entertainment for 16 years, where he produced stage shows and special events. In 1991, Kivett founded his own production company, Kivett Productions, which organizes stadium card stunts worldwide.

Kivett received a BA in speech communications and a BS in broadcast journalism from the University of Florida, and lives in downtown Orlando with his wife and daughter. They enjoy cycling, hiking and, of course, grocery shopping together.

Dr. Mark Tamplin

Dr. Tamplin holds a PhD in medical sciences, specializing in microbiology & immunology. Over a 30-year international career working as a university professor and an adjunct researcher and advisor to food-related governments, his research has explored how pathogens exist in the environment and food, and then how they cause disease in humans. Tamplin's work has been published in over 110 scientific articles and a dozen books. With his expertise in food safety and enthusiasm to educate, becoming co-author of *The Food Safety Book* was a natural fit.

Additionally, he has been appointed by the U.S. Secretary of Agriculture to serve on the National Advisory Committee on Microbiological Criteria for Foods. Early in 2016, Dr. Tamplin blended his extensive knowledge of science with adventure in *Phage*, the first novel in his science thriller trilogy. Dr. Tamplin grew up in West Virginia and now resides in Atlanta and Australia.

Dr. Gerald J. Kivett

Doctor Kivett was born in Coral Gables, Florida. He received his Bachelor of Arts degree from the University of Florida, enlisted in the U.S. Navy flight program in Pensacola, Florida, and earned his Wings of Gold in 1966. He subsequently flew with Patrol Squadron Five in Jacksonville, Florida, for four years.

He returned to the University of Florida in 1971 and received his Bachelor of Science degree, followed by his Doctor of Medicine degree in 1978. He then entered the Family Practice residency at the Naval Hospital in Jacksonville. Doctor Kivett left active duty in the Navy and started his private practice in Orlando, in 1984. He remained in the Naval Reserve and retired with the rank of Captain after twenty-four years of service.

Doctor Kivett is board certified in Family Medicine, a Fellow

of the American Academy of Family Practice, and an associ-
ate professor of Family Medicine, Florida State University
College of Medicine. He continues to stamp out disease as
a family practice doctor in Orlando today.